Crosswords For When There's No More Seinfeld To Watch

Cover image by Michelle Freer

ISBN 978-1-002-41499-6

Published by Fb &c Limited.

First Edition

First Printing 2020

www.RiddlerBooks.com

Crosswords For When There's No More Seinfeld To Watch

How to Solve Crosswords

You don't have to be a crossword expert to have a blast solving these clever puzzles! Give your brain a fantastic workout, your synapses will thank you.

The goal of the game is to fill all white squares with letters which form words or phrases, using the clues to lead you to the answers. The numbers beside each clue correspond to the numbers in the puzzle. Clues in the "Across" section are for words that are displayed horizontally in the puzzle. Clues in the "Down" section are for words that are displayed vertically.

Across

1 Word puzzles with clues (10)
5 Play with blocks, maybe (5)
6 ___ and games (3)
8 "Piece of cake" (9)
10 Collective effort (8)
15 Windows to the soul, supposedly (4)
16 Have a good trip (French) (9)

Down

2 Picture riddle (5)
3 Find the answer to a mystery (5)
4 Junction between nerve cells (7)
7 Doc's advice (4)
9 "Kaboom!" (3)
11 Have a ball (5)
12 "___ is just pink trying to be purple" (5)
13 Take it easy (5)
14 Kentucky (abbr.) (2)

Tips:

Use a pencil. It is possible to make mistakes with your guesses, by using a pencil you give yourself permission to change an answer if you end up deciding that it was not correct. Guessing is what crosswords are all about, this will only make you a better puzzler in the end.

Start with easy clues first. Don't get stuck on the first clue, start off by reading all clues to see if you find some that you can already answer. Clues that are fill in the blanks "___", anagrams "anag.", or abbreviations "abbr." can also be a good place to start.

Keep track of solved clues. This helps you focus on the remaining clues and gives you a sense of accomplishment.

Make solving social. Nothing says that you need to solve this crossword alone. Feel free to ask friends and family members for help with clues.

Don't stress. Crosswords are meant to be fun. If being stuck on a clue is becoming too frustrating, taking a break or getting some fresh air can be the perfect opportunity for one of those beloved "aha!" moments to arise.

Crossword Number 1

ACROSS

1. Largest digit (4)
2. Preppie's pop (5)
4. Lying in a flat surface (6)
6. Gladiolus-to-be (4)
10. Mourn accident, getting word about nematode (9)
11. Jerome ___, show boat composer (4)
13. A small restaurant made from calcium and iron (4)
14. What forwards get down to before starting on journey? (4)
16. It's always open in france (6)
17. Disguise under false semblance (11)
19. To-the-web hookup letters (3)
20. Make (ones way) (4)
21. Suck up again (6)

DOWN

1. Gun club: (abbr.) (3)
2. Young fowl; dress fabric (5)
3. Criticising cover audibly (7)
5. Wiring (10)
7. Troubled a degree with blue turns (11)
8. Language of the majority population of sri lanka (10)
9. One with famous last theorem (6)
12. Clouds of dust enable you finally to become obscure (7)
15. Hair-tidier (4)
17. Refuse to grant (4)
18. Slovenly person (inf) (4)

Crossword Number 2

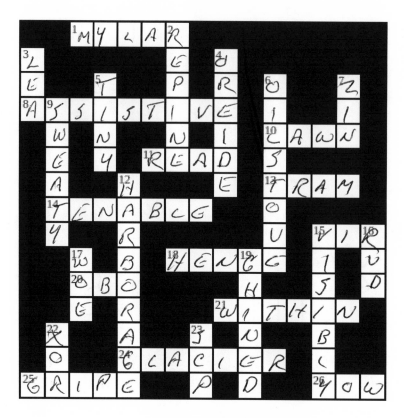

ACROSS

1. Polyester film trade name (5)
8. Workaday (9)
10. Manicuring target, often (4)
11. Enjoy the bestseller (4)
13. Monorail transport (4)
14. Reasonable / believable / plausible (7)
15. Param ___ chakra - an award and a movie too (3)
18. From this moment forward (5)
20. Or best offer (3)
21. Lets out tin whistle from the inside (6)
24. Amazingly gracile but sluggish mover (7)
25. Kvetch and grumble (5)
26. Reaction to getting burned (3)

DOWN

2. Fret about timber (6)
3. ___ and perrins (3)
4. Imitation gold (6)
5. Asian joint said to be very small (4)
6. Old-fashioned cooker (8)
7. White ___ (california wine, for short) (3)
9. We stay out, affected by the heat (6)
12. Shelter (9)
15. Evidently (7)
16. Redden (3)
17. Ah, me! feeling (3)
19. Ridged (6)
22. Country estate (3)
23. Music-industry acronym (3)

ACROSS

2. What star late for show did from the bus (6)
3. Inner hebridean isle (4)
5. Manitoba: ___/grindstone provincial park (5)
8. Boat-destroying movie creature (4)
11. Resting place (3)
12. Holiday, in roma (5)
13. Feel dejected (4)
14. Part of potus: (abbr.) (4)
15. A sudden, disastrous collapse or defeat, a fiasco (7)
19. Mean to silence baby by rocking (6)
21. Girl's hiding love of dancer (6)
22. Discovered by luck (13)

DOWN

1. In more than two ways (6)
2. Uruguayan city (5)
4. A tremor from outer space produces dots and dashes (5)
5. Horticultural trades association (3)
6. Opposite of trans (3)
7. More centralised in a plot that failed to entertain (5)
9. Miracle-___ (green thumb's product) (3)
10. Tricksier (7)
11. Usher chap on to vessel with dramatic flair (11)
12. Like 18k gold, vis-a-vis 14k gold (5)
13. Extreme unrest (6)
16. Some smokes (6)
17. Laundry holder, briefly (4)
18. What fuzzy wuzzy was (5)
20. Drill user, briefly (3)

Crossword Number 4

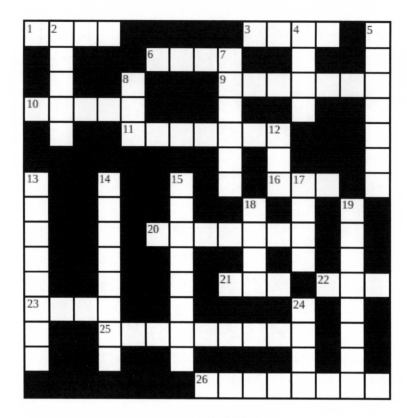

ACROSS

1. Girl invited into the garden in song (4)
3. Petit-de-___, n.s. (4)
6. Note that is about large setting for aida (4)
9. Healing (7)
10. Time, rhythm (5)
11. Industrial strike (7)
16. Old fireproofing material: (abbr.) (3)
20. Internal organs of a fowl (7)
21. Ford motor co. model (3)
22. Joe, in (3)
23. No, in vladivostak (4)
25. Logically showing eve isnt so bad (9)
26. Chinese umbrella material (8)

DOWN

2. Alvin who choreographed revelations (5)
4. Thanks ___ '! (tonnes of appreciation!) (4)
5. Causing harm (7)
7. Give form to (idea) (6)
8. Ka-boom (3)
12. Cigar city, on baggage (3)
13. Island near michigan (8)
14. Yet he doesn't work at a carvery (8)
15. Panic just when entering swamp (8)
17. Ancient city in south america (4)
18. Tome's attribute (4)
19. The height of aviation (8)
24. Variable film supported by a character in patras (4)

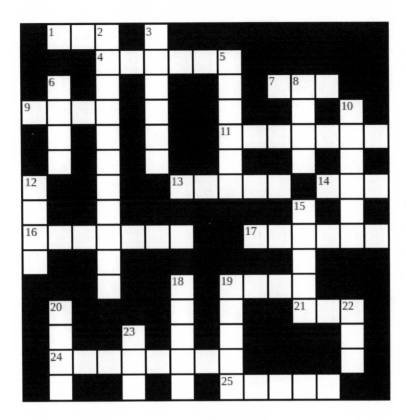

ACROSS

1. Texting format (3)
4. Belonging to an incisor or molar, say (6)
7. Drill user, briefly (3)
9. Soda with caffeine (4)
11. Orange-yellow, mostly tropical bananas (7)
13. Indeterminate vowel sound (5)
14. Expert touch (3)
16. At no great cost (7)
17. Particle beam weapon (6)
19. Tipplers' road infractions: (abbr.) (4)
21. Czech religious reformer jan (3)
24. Being stubborn about red revolution (8)
25. A look (5)

DOWN

2. Law imposed by the military (11)
3. Reproduced (6)
5. Flatten a gourd (6)
6. Look at cover for serious deficit (4)
8. Wound severely (4)
10. To revolve (6)
12. Fire bag (4)
15. Abusive, possibly rash after a hasty start (5)
18. Drawling statesman! (5)
19. Challenged about father being outside (5)
20. One of a trio at either end of a quidditch pitch (4)
22. Call from a sinking ship (3)
23. Swiss canton (3)

Crossword Number 6

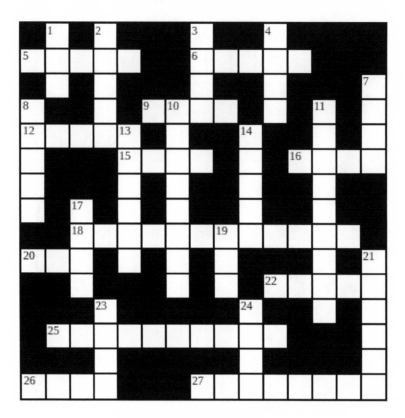

ACROSS

5. Hymn (5)
6. Ancient port of greece (5)
9. Bounces back from railway incident (4)
12. Wide world of sports host jim (5)
15. Smell, in toledo (4)
16. Twice-monthly 7-down (4)
18. Guise (12)
20. Baboon heart recipient baby ___ (3)
22. Eskimo snow house (5)
25. Nco was most upset by celt (10)
26. Black eye initially violet, forming bruise on skin (4)
27. Lava, blue version, that is worth something (8)

DOWN

1. Remote raf manoeuvre (3)
2. Vestment viewed as excessive in the golden state (5)
3. Town in galilee (4)
4. Tree of the tilia genus (4)
7. Make frothy and light (4)
8. Specks of soot (5)
10. Narrow-minded person takes on rubbish project (8)
11. With emotion (9)
13. Indian philosophy based on yoga (6)
14. 20 (5)
17. Footnotes' the same (4)
19. Beantown team, for short (3)
21. Herb and salad plant (6)
23. Feel dejected (4)
24. Colorado ski resort (4)

Crossword Number 7

ACROSS

1. Bit of soot (3)
7. Any in let out, naturally (8)
9. Australian tree (5)
11. Mexican dough (4)
13. Flabbergasted with obe nevertheless (7)
16. Letter for one young suffolk lawyer (6)
17. Manicure boards (7)
18. Cheers robin (4)
20. Either kept striking or worked hard (7)
21. Showing, as a card (6)
25. Common sheet fabric (7)
26. Tv's li'l sound button (3)
27. Brooding and frowning (4)

DOWN

2. English glam-rock band with six #1 hits (4)
3. Occupation (12)
4. Fall heavily and limply (5)
5. Secretly: sub ___ (4)
6. Pin-entering place to get dollars (3)
8. It's periodically listed, yet strange to find one included (7)
10. Tut's place (4)
12. Place giving protection (7)
14. More apt to snap (7)
15. Comic actor gene (6)
19. Borough in east greater london (6)
22. Comrade (3)
23. At, tamen (3)
24. Manhattan sch. (3)

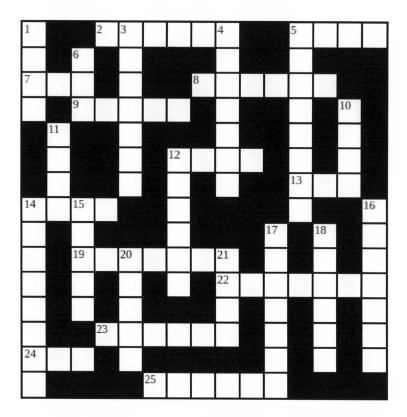

ACROSS

2. She plays joyce on "stranger things" (6)
5. Cologne (gr.) (4)
7. Tee neck style (3)
8. Lycidas poet (6)
9. Make frog noises (5)
12. Agnes ___, anne bronte novel (4)
13. Court order (init) (3)
14. Cultural celebration (4)
19. Most distinguished head in case (7)
22. Balance with skill in new launch (7)
23. Unnamed publication or person (6)
24. Starting point of a golf hole (3)
25. Simple form of mixed language (6)

DOWN

1. Cover for vehicles (4)
3. How speakers make a statement? (7)
4. Mechanic or orthodontist, at times (7)
5. Weather formation over a mountain (8)
6. Hero of hardboiled fiction (3)
10. This-and-that mixture (4)
11. Old invader of england prepared for sacking (4)
12. One who overeats (6)
14. Service's founder to close large town's front before the rest (8)
15. Irish riders to the sea playwright (5)
16. Former (7)
17. Not revealed (7)
18. U.s. navy construction battalion member (6)
20. Another name for sesame (5)
21. Monorail transport (4)

Crossword Number 9

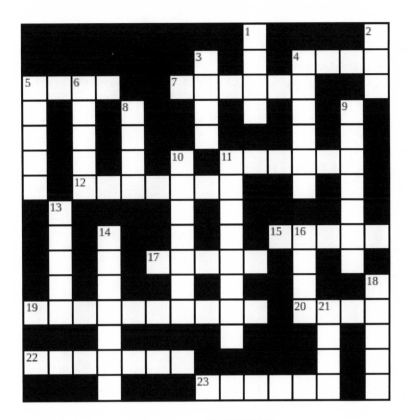

ACROSS

4. Muslim chief (4)
5. Road manager's always on it, for short (4)
7. Artistically depicts one taking rubbish out (6)
11. Crystalline amino acid (6)
12. Amateur baseball field (7)
15. Like poison (5)
17. Pest involved with current ill will (5)
19. Nail pro (10)
20. Dare, colloquially (4)
22. Champagne and peach juice for painter (7)
23. Australian crane (6)

DOWN

1. Undergraduate eng. degree (4)
2. Limited mil. assignment (3)
3. Hardly thrill-filled (4)
4. Inner layer of the periosteum (6)
5. Talk about new slogan (5)
6. Tennyson's the ___-eaters (5)
8. To prove guilty (4)
9. ___ era (when players were juiced) (7)
10. Tv blunder (coll) (7)
11. Ask one's mum about being a bit thick (8)
13. Skier's maneuver (5)
14. Very large small implement, bone and say very (7)
16. Ot bk. after amos (4)
18. Sporty ford, to aficionados (5)
21. 'waterloo' pop group (4)

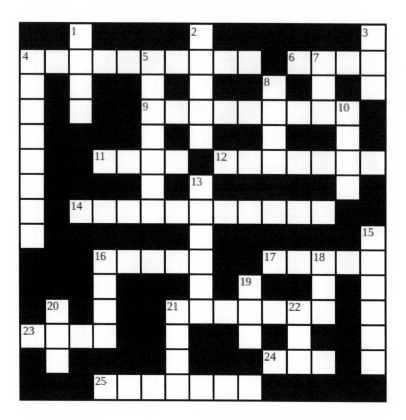

ACROSS

4. Infielders confused fans? (10)
6. Language teacher has again impressed beginners (4)
9. The ___,2009 horror starring emily browning and arielle kebbel (9)
11. From china one ancient language (4)
12. City on the clyde and its tributary, kelvin (7)
14. Writing (11)
16. Nelle in ally mcbeal, portia de ___ (5)
17. They can be jammed up (5)
21. Stalk remover (7)
23. Old brit. coins (4)
24. Slangy affirmation, variantly (3)
25. The tympanic membrane (7)

DOWN

1. Kindle read, briefly (4)
2. Imitate, ape (5)
3. Retract (3)
4. With a frondy look (8)
5. Hitchhiker's guide author, - adams (7)
7. Get cracking, archaically (3)
8. Wild mango (4)
10. Pairs of singers (4)
13. Begone, to shakespeare (6)
15. The wallpaper girl (6)
16. Niminy-piminy person (4)
18. Second-ride freebie: (abbr.) (3)
19. White house accounting gp. (3)
20. Letter of the hebrew alphabet (3)
21. Glided smoothly (4)
22. She tasted the forbidden fruit (3)

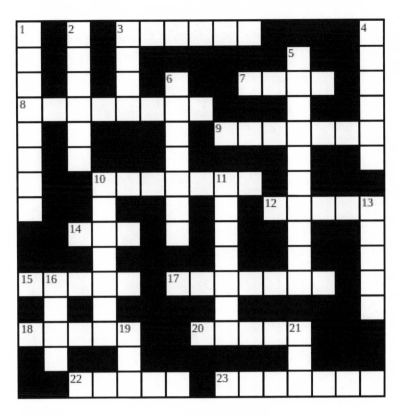

ACROSS

3. Silly person not right is held to be petty (6)
7. Campsite shelter for some forgotten troop (4)
8. Worn after rowing? (8)
9. Apian (7)
10. As if in shock (7)
12. Mecca's seaport (5)
14. Arc sound (3)
15. Rose from slumber, old-style (5)
17. One interpreting cipher (7)
18. Outstanding lesson (5)
20. Vermeer and rembrandt contemporary (5)
22. Id cover (5)
23. Colourings (7)

DOWN

1. Taking a photo, say (8)
2. Limner (anag.) (6)
3. A certain monetary unit (4)
4. Near land's end? shut up! (6)
5. Stiff (10)
6. Very closely (7)
10. Storage for artists (7)
11. Kind of engraving (7)
13. Not concurrent in time: (abbr.) (5)
16. The breakfast club star sheedy (4)
19. Slide and almost lose control of car (3)
21. Nest (fr.) (3)

Crossword Number 12

ACROSS

1. Lunar period (5)
5. Salem's setting: (abbr.) (3)
6. Readily separating mineral (4)
7. Inhale through the nose (5)
10. Rights (10)
13. Wholeness (8)
14. Suffix to 'synth' (4)
18. Tooled (7)
19. Some cough medicine: var. (5)
21. Ridiculously foolish (9)
22. Saying (8)

DOWN

1. No wall in stairwells or in the abbey (6)
2. Enjoy a lake (4)
3. End part of a sleeve (4)
4. Action from city against hearts, maybe, with breaks (7)
7. Pouty moods (5)
8. Denizen of the leaning tower city (5)
9. No-one is on the port - it's all gone! (4)
11. Sallying out in a remarkable way (8)
12. Ovid's Io! (4)
15. Make drinkable, as seawater (6)
16. Us dish of boiled maize kernels (5)
17. Adhesive substance son squeezed into part of tack (5)
20. Solid figure is put right in front in the afternoon (5)

Crossword Number 13

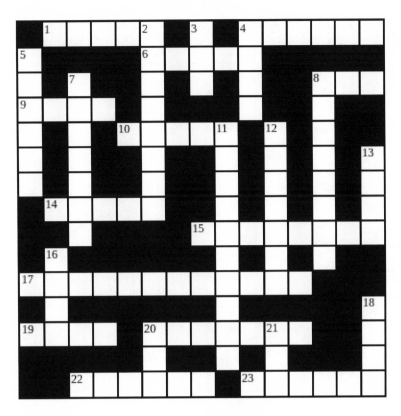

ACROSS

1. A sect reserved for a social class (5)
4. X- this clue isn't! (6)
6. Fictional animal hunted by lewis carroll? (5)
8. Klinger's rank: (abbr.) (3)
9. Wear away by biting (4)
10. Chief standing bear's tribe (5)
14. Denizen of the leaning tower city (5)
15. Energy, enthusiasm (8)
17. Vilifying (12)
19. Ricardo arjona album "5to ___" (4)
20. Big wheel actor danson, the opposite of tolerant (7)
22. Valued (6)
23. ___ wesker, playwright (6)

DOWN

2. Ingredient in some oral contraceptives (8)
3. Zodiac animal with horns (3)
4. Like or similar (4)
5. Baghdad's river (6)
7. Great deal! (7)
8. Wooden-shoe folk dance (8)
11. Assignment (10)
12. Begin on canal (7)
13. Kind of light? extremely! (4)
16. Islamic judge (4)
18. Quantity of firewood (4)
20. Stand in against a pitcher (3)
21. Old testament book before neh. (3)

Crossword Number 14

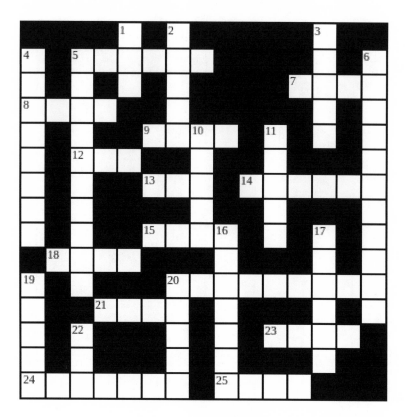

ACROSS

5. Uses a norelco (6)
7. Give birth to a lamb or kid (4)
8. Animal hair left in jam (4)
9. Collectively neither one thing nor the other (4)
12. Aunt's/uncle's child (archaic) (3)
13. The godfather's backing band (3)
14. Sword, in seville (6)
15. 150 overdose on dirt (4)
18. Sub weapon (4)
20. Somewhere (9)
21. ___ love her (beatles) (4)
23. Source of a nightmare (4)
24. Perfect miserable answer about cause of pallor (7)
25. Elegant little bird without a tail (4)

DOWN

1. Coffee enquiry: '... or decaf?' (3)
2. Dry wine left by professional (5)
3. To line up (5)
4. Spread over a wide area (8)
5. Herb as son, little chap with endless merit (10)
6. Tiny insect-eating bird (11)
10. Awfully big day coming up for old poet (5)
11. Eccentric got us relish (5)
16. Possessed by a devil (7)
17. In two dimensions (6)
19. California mission founder junipero (5)
20. Sort of spruce in british columbia (5)
22. Japan's 59th emperor (3)

Crossword Number 15

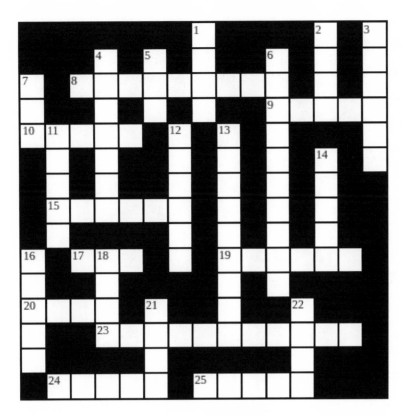

ACROSS

8. Radiating (9)
9. Talk gibberish (5)
10. Anklebone can be fixed in hospital usually (5)
15. The ascension of a celestial object at the same time as the sun (6)
17. Wimbledon sports body (3)
19. Article is about russia and what belongs to them (6)
20. City in kansai, japan; capital of the country from 710-784 (4)
23. Primeval ostrich ripe for reconstruction (11)
24. Porous pot (5)
25. Genus of (5)

DOWN

1. Feature that bars the southeast (4)
2. Uno menos uno, to unamuno (4)
3. In an 'aww'-inspiring manner (6)
4. Leg bones (7)
5. Ex-gis'gp. (3)
6. Spurned (10)
7. Rubbish in a bad state (3)
11. Blue sky color (5)
12. Twisted (6)
13. One with sixteen wheels carrying international concerns (9)
14. States-style knight's protection (5)
16. A last look at alf in confusion (5)
18. It was part of a duck plant (4)
21. Unix scripting language (4)
22. Stiffly formal and precise (person or manner) (4)

Crossword Number 16

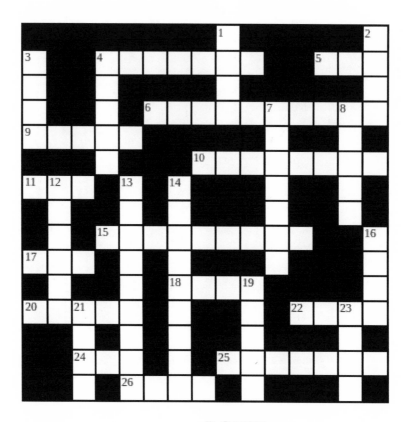

ACROSS

4. A bit less length pleasing to the eye (7)
5. Part of c.p.i. (3)
6. Yelled (10)
9. Tiny spot or mark (5)
10. Sculptor's preliminary model (8)
11. ___ name it (3)
15. Meals (9)
17. 'oklahoma!' baddie (3)
18. Barge firm in the southwest (4)
20. Flee above board (5)
22. Porkchops, e.g. (4)
24. Vodka or gin: (abbr.) (3)
25. Six feet, two inches, e.g. (7)
26. Planner, for short (4)

DOWN

1. Woodwind instr. (4)
2. What the little dutch boy stuck his finger in, in a kid's story (4)
3. Gang's home (4)
4. Item in a kitchen rack (5)
7. Camera lens cover (7)
8. Grouse hiding head in wild plant (5)
12. Fancy us to be stupid (6)
13. The science of sound (9)
14. Fisherman's spot, sometimes (9)
16. Dare, old style english (4)
19. Shrivel from age (5)
21. One of three in a hat trick (4)
23. Wwii's battle of ___ (4)

Crossword Number 17

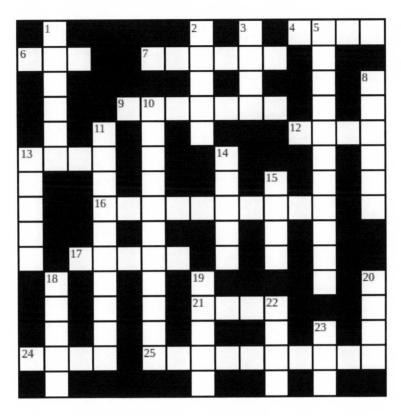

ACROSS

4. Tall marsh plant (4)
6. React emotionally when retired manager loses son (3)
7. Hot dog, slangily (var.) (6)
9. Banned supplement (7)
12. In a shortened way this month (4)
13. Abe's coin (4)
16. Simultaneous (10)
17. Stared with awe (5)
21. Flap and shot (4)
24. Tooth fairy's first name, inscribed in silver (4)
25. Jet set (10)

DOWN

1. 16 straddling california and nevada (6)
2. Cut, chopped (5)
3. Unit of currency in ethiopia (4)
5. Realistic (11)
8. Town near boston (6)
10. Dogged (11)
11. Walling (10)
13. The beach (5)
14. 48th u.s. vp (5)
15. Sweet jester (4)
18. Title character in 1826 j f cooper novel the last of the mohicans (5)
19. Balkans river (5)
20. Met me leaving and enquire about a job (4)
22. Obsolete submachine gun (4)
23. ___ jones (stock index) (3)

Crossword Number 18

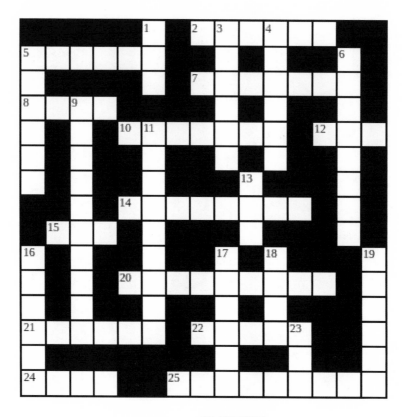

ACROSS

2. Apple seed, something sharp at one end (6)
5. Sleeping beauty protagonist (6)
7. Memorable painter. (7)
8. ___-rooter (pipe unclogger) (4)
10. Side view for the record (7)
12. Arbitrary term in a series (3)
14. Cures / solutions / fixes (8)
15. Trim, short guy from warsaw returns (3)
20. Rendered in tiny dots (9)
21. Fast food's leader producing whopper? (6)
22. Without much energy (5)
24. Captain or colonel, for example (4)
25. Unfed, yell out in way reflecting poverty (9)

DOWN

1. Which body processes applications for third-level education? (3)
3. 60-across's home (6)
4. Provide provisions (6)
5. Decided jointly (6)
6. Bleached, like teeth (8)
9. Bulge (10)
11. Giving away the spanish vinegar recipe (9)
13. ___ ' ___ for london (3)
16. Moccasin-type shoe (6)
17. Cut stick (6)
18. Regulated co. (4)
19. Very tall (6)
23. ___ name it (3)

Crossword Number 19

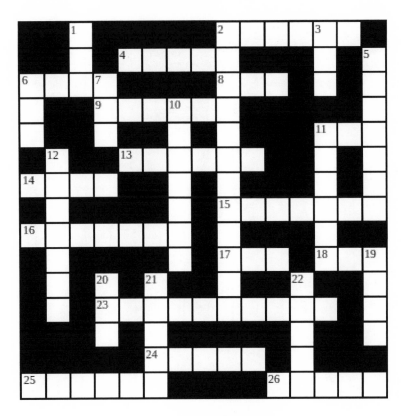

ACROSS

2. South american grasslands (6)
4. Town near palm springs (5)
6. Blue dye from plants (4)
8. Emerald point ___ (3)
9. Some 'daddy', nasty sort of ruler (6)
11. Clinging seed case (3)
13. Red wine in summer lottery (6)
14. University lecturer, for short (4)
15. Imposing (tax) (7)
16. Commuting group (7)
17. Shedding neckwear (3)
18. Tyrian purple, e.g. (3)
23. Impeccably (10)
24. Barker and luthor (5)
25. A little time with empty hour, i have to prosper (6)
26. Microwave laser (5)

DOWN

1. River to the south china sea (3)
2. Docile (12)
3. Palindromic kitchen brand (3)
5. Loving song and dance band (7)
6. Currency unit of 18 down (3)
7. Person in charge : (abbr.) (3)
10. A serial about receivers (7)
11. Surround or encompass (6)
12. Made, generated (7)
19. Well done! (4)
20. Complete loon (3)
21. Ball in france (5)
22. Puffball part (5)

Crossword Number 20

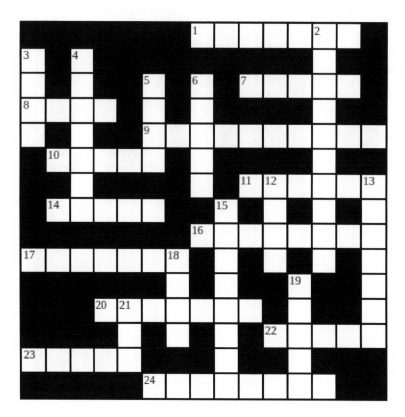

ACROSS

1. Afflicted, harassed (7)
7. Bnai ___ (5)
8. One of the traditional kingdoms of uganda (4)
9. Scheming (10)
10. Pop art interjection (5)
11. Stud feature (6)
14. Tony-winner uta - (5)
16. Quality found in mantillas (8)
17. Areas between hills, especially in south wales (7)
20. Wheeling (7)
22. Public school that featured in tom brown's school days (5)
23. City nw of detroit (5)
24. American cake topping (8)

DOWN

2. Disentangled english tax credit incorrectly (10)
3. Some "night court" characters: (abbr.) (4)
4. The technical name for smallpox (7)
5. Writer andre (4)
6. Potters' media (5)
12. Sch. leader (4)
13. Refuse to take orders (7)
15. Wellness (8)
18. Way or method : (abbr.) (4)
19. Deplore doctor having to run off (5)
21. Statue meas. (3)

Crossword Number 21

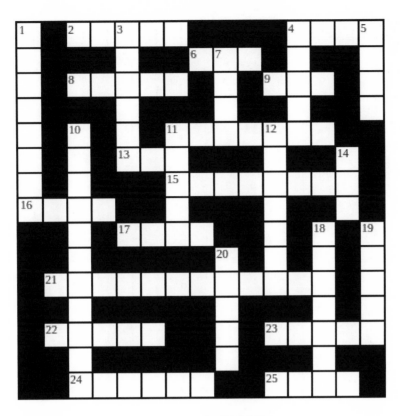

ACROSS

2. Papers, tv etc (5)
4. Nap spot, perhaps (4)
6. The bee gees' old record label (3)
8. Violin, e.g. (5)
9. Cask: (abbr.) (3)
11. Wreckage floating on sea (7)
13. Hard: french (3)
15. Special honour or recognition of merit (8)
16. Call of ___ (4)
17. Deity of monotheistic cult (4)
21. Pertaining to a country's rulers (12)
22. Attached to the top of your willow tree (5)
23. Chuck out wild civet (5)
24. Go over broken rut (6)
25. Subdue at a riot, informally (4)

DOWN

1. Serious girl was thinking (8)
3. Green alga (6)
4. Province in north central spain (5)
5. Oct. pennant race (4)
7. One of the solomon islands (4)
10. Next to each other (11)
11. Case or border enclosing a picture, window, door (5)
12. Ask or tout for (7)
14. Acrossmarry (3)
18. Harness drivers' places (7)
19. Hair damaged by breaking at the tips (5)
20. The ponder heart author (5)

Crossword Number 22

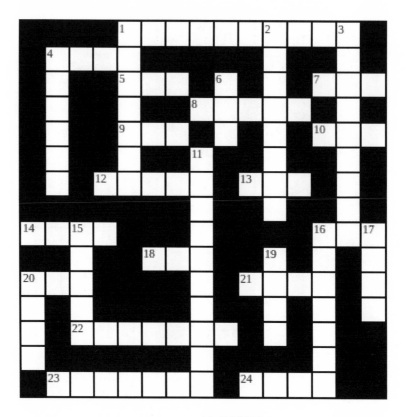

ACROSS

1. I did it for one broadcast and then another and another! (10)
4. ___ curriculum (set of courses taken by all students) (4)
5. There's an ___ for that (3)
7. Where michael jordan played coll. ball (3)
8. Form of the arabic alphabet (5)
9. Channel that airs "cake boss" (3)
10. Pouch one almost gets on being dismissed (3)
12. Grand mosque locale (5)
13. Part of s& l: (abbr.) (3)
14. Elisabeth ___, peggy in mad men (4)
16. A bit of a fidget, you understand (3)
18. Missile initials (3)
20. Checking acct. figure (3)
21. More than average height (4)
22. In 26 without, say, a type of hat (7)
23. Not 12 (7)
24. Simpson with a high i.q. (4)

DOWN

1. Us city on the isthmus between lake washington and puget sound (7)
2. Distribution of banned literature in soviet russia (8)
3. Not aboriginal (9)
4. Oval bacterium (6)
6. Clone or copy, curtly (3)
11. Overplaying (10)
15. Alternative name for the county of shropshire (5)
16. American girl one spies in part of spain (7)
17. Hardly thrill-filled (4)
19. El ___; john payne western movie (4)
20. A range of frequencies or wavelengths between two limits (4)

Crossword Number 23

ACROSS

1. 36 out of 88 (7)
3. Artificial rubber (4)
5. Admitting viewpoint, theologian was suspended (7)
8. Native of 22-across (3)
9. Status ___ ; ___ vadis (3)
11. Composer of salome and elektra (7)
15. Weighted (10)
16. Navy sub initials (3)
17. Is he petty on board in charge of present stores? (7)
19. No fuddy-duddy (3)
20. Bit of compensation for the writer (3)
22. Order of whales, etc (7)
25. Poet's 'repeatedly' (3)
26. Say euro is around about $1,000, gross (9)
27. Gasteyer who was on saturday night live from 1996 to 2002 (3)

DOWN

2. Cartoonish gunshot sound (4)
3. Refried fare (5)
4. An occasion when the sun is furthest from the equator (8)
6. Treasured item (3)
7. 2004 fantasy romcom with anne hathaway and hugh dancy (9)
10. Provoke into hostility (10)
12. Book written to myself (4)
13. Moose genus (5)
14. Mortar beaters (4)
18. Affected coyness, with the (5)
19. Monetary unit of vietnam o ha (anag.)? (3)
21. Watchful person (4)
23. Grafting shoot (4)
24. Twice (mus) (3)

Crossword Number 24

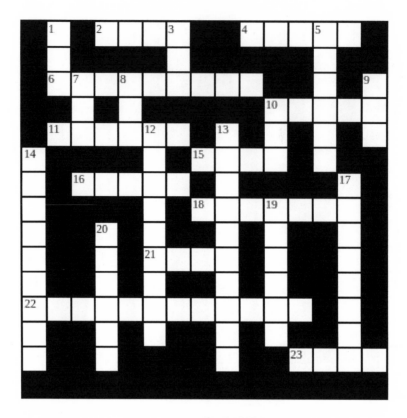

ACROSS

2. Goodbye! time to catch a monster! (4)
4. Town near dunstable (5)
6. Church attendees (9)
10. Chuck, it seems, is of doubtful worth! (5)
11. Jazz pianist and composer, jelly roll ___ (6)
15. Dark 17-across (4)
16. Stares in wonder (5)
18. Heartfelt in the extreme - real touching (7)
21. Cold cryptid (4)
22. Voted (12)
23. Sharp or sour in flavour (4)

DOWN

1. Mean sea level: (abbr.) (3)
3. Genevabased workers' rights gp. (3)
5. You've never seen this king with a tattered robe on (6)
7. Turku, in sweden (3)
8. Card players can stand it (3)
9. Leatherman's tool (3)
10. He wants paul, in his protection from the wet (3)
12. On top of being too trendy, also grand (9)
13. Yodeling (10)
14. Sprucest (9)
17. Nappier (8)
19. Humdrummer (6)
20. System of aircraft navigation (6)

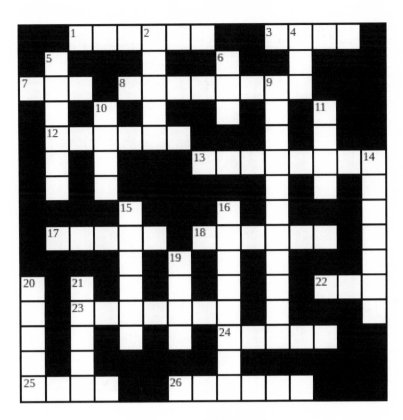

ACROSS

1. He has touching habits (6)
3. Words of departure (4)
7. Port.'s home (3)
8. Rule (8)
12. React, ordering and quaffing large wine (6)
13. Battery-powered (phone) (8)
17. Like the days of yore (5)
18. *before - flour, water, shortening; after - ___ (6)
22. Literally, shady side (3)
23. Style of coiffure (7)
24. Old people in cut-price nightwear (5)
25. Had too much, in brief (4)
26. Just claims to have heard liturgies (6)

DOWN

2. Kiss fits like a ___ (5)
4. Get at the store (3)
5. Fish that lacks scales (6)
6. Start walking back, as a rule (3)
9. Hired soldier (11)
10. One of a ketch's two (4)
11. Lone type of a man (4)
14. Neapolitan alternative (7)
15. Type of campfire roast (6)
16. Youth leader taking steps to restrict husband's sport (8)
19. Invoice info, ___. no. (4)
20. ___ modelo (beer brand) (5)
21. Those people ultimately rule subject (5)

Crossword Number 26

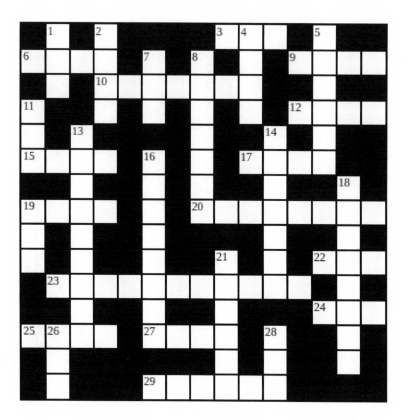

ACROSS

3. An association of registered nurses in the philippines (3)
6. Like goji berry plants (4)
9. Long chinese dynasty (4)
10. Best ventilated (7)
12. Turn on the ice (4)
15. Grandfather has money in south africa (4)
17. Confusion about unknown term of imprecation (4)
19. Dog in a series of children's books by eric hill (4)
20. Spread uncontrollably (8)
22. Quebec's largest city : (abbr.) (3)
23. Garmented (11)
24. Petri dish site (3)
25. Former porn star ___ olson (4)
27. Right behind blue cheese (4)
29. Lego pieces (6)

DOWN

1. ___ ' ___ in newfoundland (3)
2. Year in prison shade (4)
4. They're edible, like bananas (4)
5. Defraud (6)
7. Something a doc might order (3)
8. Harpsichord (7)
11. What / might signify (3)
13. Spur along (9)
14. Offering lots of roughage (7)
16. Sound intensity (8)
18. Low pass in game (8)
19. Backward throw (3)
21. Visigothic king (6)
26. Not elective: (abbr.) (3)
28. Advantages for job seekers (3)

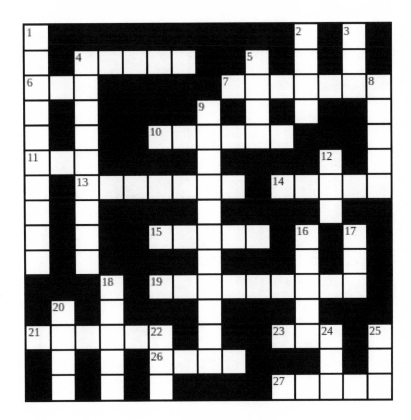

ACROSS

4. Discourage daughter and parent's sister (5)
6. Grocery chain (3)
7. Dewy quality (7)
10. New mexico's ___ national labs (6)
11. Traditional scandinavian rug (3)
13. Torrid zone (7)
14. Photograph new growth (5)
15. King of a wild horde (5)
19. Get behind with revising, being ignorant (9)
21. Former county now in powys (6)
23. Air data comp. (3)
26. Elephant appendage (4)
27. Tenacious (5)

DOWN

1. Academic establishment (10)
2. Fifty's five (4)
3. Beverly ___, ca (3)
4. Sinistral (9)
5. Lucille's classic sitcom partner (4)
8. Flowed out of a container especially accidentally (5)
9. Oldfashioned (11)
12. Wild thing by tone-___ (3)
16. Being so unpopular, had to get out of some hotel (5)
17. Rope-splicing implement (3)
18. Snack (5)
20. Did like the titanic (4)
22. Somewhat rundown (3)
24. Tron program (3)
25. She starts and finishes monday (3)

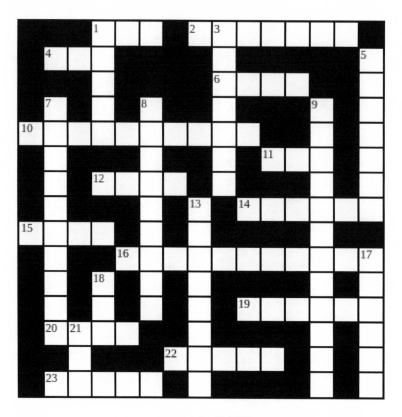

ACROSS

1. Lawyer's deg. (3)
2. A little fossil, very lustrous white (7)
4. Central asiatic tent (3)
6. Hit clumsy fellow lying about a deception (4)
10. Assert the opposite of (a statement) (10)
11. What mos. and mos. add up to (3)
12. Gas that's used to illuminate signs (4)
14. Synchronized speaker's shaken (6)
15. Nip the top off the measurement (4)
16. Participation (in something) (11)
19. Of a mind to mention it, on withdrawal (6)
20. Miserable german left with hesitation (4)
22. Small genus of eurasian aquatic perennial herbs. (5)
23. Wrinkle removing injection (5)

DOWN

1. J. edgar director eastwood (5)
3. Odysseus, by birth (7)
5. Frontward (7)
7. Worn (10)
8. Union dropouts of '61 (9)
9. Not aware of present danger (12)
13. Voracious larval corn pest (8)
17. Rich powerful person (6)
18. Japanese catch up guyanese hosts (3)
21. Bog room (3)

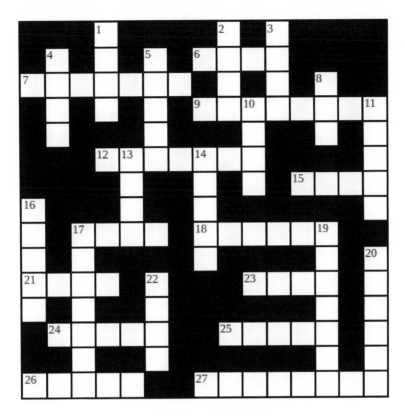

ACROSS

6. Sacred writing of hinduism (4)
7. Delivered notes - supplied prompt (7)
9. Incendiary (8)
12. Copper coatings (7)
15. Ill-acquired funds (4)
17. Se nigerian people (4)
18. Like a powerful checker (6)
21. Wharf or pier (4)
23. Shelter posh african (4)
24. The man from the mayfair wineshop (5)
25. Six in one are sheep-like (5)
26. Opec vip, variantly (5)
27. Carpentry workshop support (8)

DOWN

1. Random house vol. (4)
2. Blessed, in paris (4)
3. Joke involving judge and parrot (4)
4. Bold, skillful thing (4)
5. Ultimately bored by issue, resign (5)
8. Chaney who played the phantom (3)
10. Crisp bread for baby (4)
11. Great, in retro reviews (5)
13. Archaeological shelter (4)
14. ___campbell, scottish radio and tv presenter (5)
16. ___ bus, long single decker (5)
17. Talk aimlessly (7)
19. A bribe (7)
20. Land, having hoofed one back, edible shellfish (6)
22. Loretta with the pipes (4)

ACROSS

2. Money-lender receiving pence he takes unlawfully (7)
4. Group of fliers intially start a journey (6)
7. Feat of great daring (5)
9. Not as vigorous (7)
11. Little auk ripping heart out of fish (4)
13. Chicago terminal code (3)
14. Labor gp. that focuses on metal (3)
15. Rode a bicycle (7)
18. Apple with fungal disease mostly covering batch (6)
20. Like the mojave's climate (4)
23. Diminutive girl that is supporting bazaar (5)
25. Tight-fitting high-necked chinese dress (9)
26. Ddt successor (4)

DOWN

1. Notes from stockholm (6)
3. Worths (9)
5. A mineral for fever ___ or fighting practice (9)
6. Skilful, having some earthenware left out (4)
8. Rearward (10)
10. First person from leeds playing the lead (6)
12. Cartoonish gunshot sound (4)
16. Barnaby ___', novel by charles dickens (5)
17. James of the disaster artist (6)
19. Junky e-mail (4)
21. Texting format (3)
22. Magazine edition, for short (3)
24. 17th letter's spelling (3)

Crossword Number 31

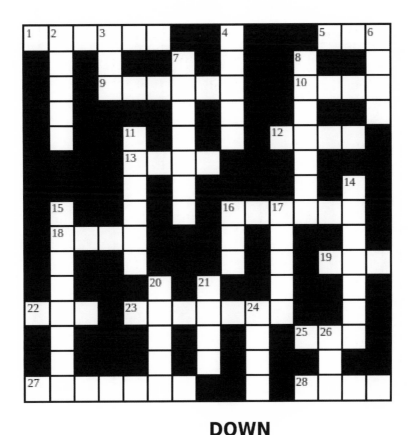

ACROSS

1. Take notice, at having entered, of having raised the temperature (6)
5. Caramel candies from hershey (3)
9. Softest (6)
10. Dodgers pitcher rodriguez (4)
12. I-95, e.g. (4)
13. Promoted capt. (4)
16. Provided a synopsis (6)
18. Reserve heading off in pain (4)
19. Bollywood's raja ___ rank (3)
22. Announcement: (abbr.) (3)
23. 'stone' in ireland (7)
25. Was given leave, starting tomorrow (3)
27. Long-reigning prince is less dry (7)
28. Gentiles (4)

DOWN

2. Of a great lake (5)
3. Woollen cap (3)
4. Fido does this (5)
6. Below, to a sailor (4)
7. With all the dressings removed? (7)
8. Witty adage (7)
11. Reduced growth of fruit at end of orchard (6)
14. Person subordinate to another (7)
15. Girl hiding drink in pouches (8)
16. Ford explorer, for one [acronym] (3)
17. Unlike rolling stones, supposedly (5)
20. Goosefoot plant disease is reported (5)
21. South park's parker (4)
24. Employee stock ownership plan (4)
26. Palindromic war on poverty agcy. (3)

Crossword Number 32

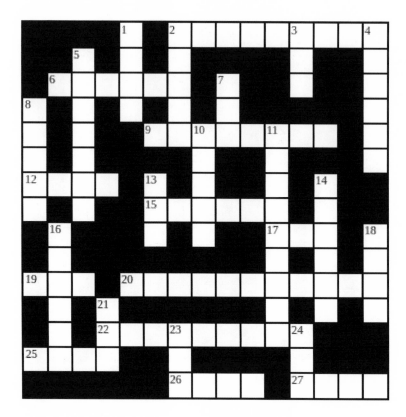

ACROSS

2. Garbage disposal (9)
6. Plastered (with) (6)
9. Wittier (8)
12. The wiz classic "___ on down the road" (4)
15. Eli's rival (6)
17. Suffix with chlor (3)
19. Fenway team: (abbr.) (3)
20. Wantoning (11)
22. Composer noted for canon in d (9)
25. Bbc tv series about raising money, ___ in the attic (4)
26. Little fields creature (4)
27. A protuberance of the mammary gland through which milk passes (4)

DOWN

1. Toronto's shoe museum (4)
2. Native louisianans (5)
3. Our version of nasa, est. 1989 (3)
4. Green i spotted between river and lake, spring back (6)
5. Not particularly hard (7)
7. Apricot-like japanese fruit (3)
8. Traveled by greyhound (5)
10. ___ board, card for stretching stitching (5)
11. Lie over (9)
13. Drug used in some laced joints (3)
14. Animate (6)
16. Cylindrically-stemmed cactus (6)
18. A sharply directional antenna. (4)
21. Us driving speed meas. (3)
23. Bug that might develop into aids (3)
24. Li'l edmonton transport (3)

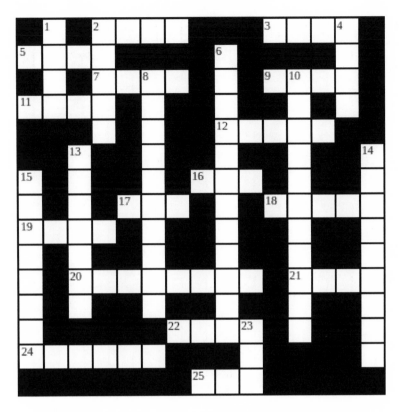

ACROSS

2. Minor misfire (4)
3. To kick (4)
5. Thing stuck to paper (4)
7. The end of a nameless italian, maybe (4)
9. I'd appear in opposite directions as an extra (4)
11. Bangladeshi currency (4)
12. Scythe handle (5)
16. Squeaky dog sound (3)
17. She starts and finishes monday (3)
18. A maasai warrior (5)
19. Spanish celery (4)
20. Send out, broadcast (8)
21. Hoppy brews, for short (4)
22. Capital equipment on the east of libya (4)
24. Surrounded, in olden times (6)
25. G.i. watchdogs (3)

DOWN

1. ___ carvey, comedian (4)
2. Curled up (5)
4. Excessively sentimental message shortened (4)
6. Validating (12)
8. Planning (10)
10. Like some memos (11)
13. Glut (7)
14. Surveyed scans a&e produced over 5d (9)
15. Right-wing partys friend concealing hot wrath endlessly (8)
23. Muscles in your "core" (3)

Crossword Number 34

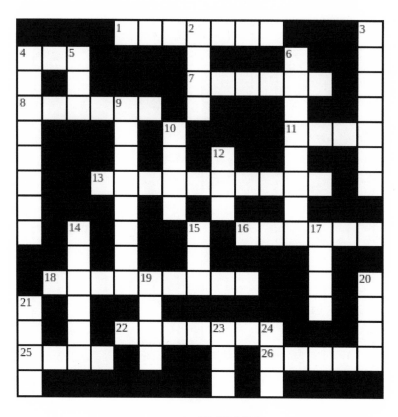

ACROSS

1. Honoring (7)
4. Compass dir. (3)
7. Dramatic entertainment popular in the 16th and 17th centuries (6)
8. Less-traveled way (6)
11. Small enclosure (4)
13. Feminist lessons (10)
16. With deep tracks (6)
18. Wrangle (9)
22. Census unit, in cordoba (7)
25. 'puttin' on the -' (4)
26. Town in eastern france, noted for an eponymous mustard variety (5)

DOWN

2. Drug also known as ecstasy (4)
3. Pindaric ode stanza (7)
4. Assimilate, in israel (8)
5. Statistic commonly used to measure an economys performance. (3)
6. (of fruit) most moist (8)
9. Be dictated to and remove it (8)
10. Be obliged to (4)
12. A tittle (3)
14. Tight-fitting undergarment (6)
15. Christmas bowlful (3)
17. Cover by unpatriotic group of musicians (4)
19. Weather research agcy. (4)
20. Charles ii's beloved nell (4)
21. Fish without water absorbs oxygen (4)
23. Address: (abbr.) (3)
24. B'nai b'rith grp. (3)

Crossword Number 35

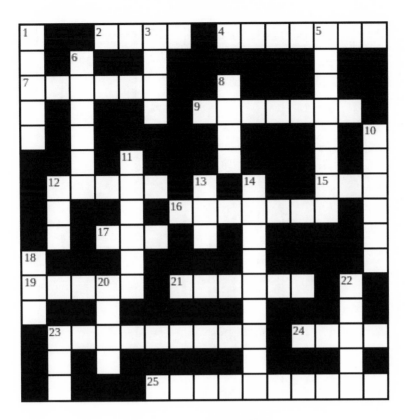

ACROSS

2. Carry off (obs) (4)
4. Cut into a cliff (7)
7. Coarse-grained rock; sounds like agreeable (6)
9. Rope of eighteen inches? less than that (7)
12. Bear onset of business collapse (5)
15. Water flow meas. (3)
16. Fancy a hundred and thirty days on frozen water? (7)
17. Rd. with tolls (3)
19. Pale and with fluctuating energy (5)
21. Inuit dish of whale skin and blubber (6)
23. Knifelike (9)
24. A shirt tag may irritate it (4)
25. Confusion, bewilderment (10)

DOWN

1. Word that's old found in records (5)
3. ___ kumar, comedian (4)
5. Deteriorate (8)
6. Cattleman, at times (6)
8. Announce red alert (4)
10. Actors join the french piece (6)
11. Drink of alcohol (6)
12. Part was effective (3)
13. Acorn, in time (3)
14. Pre-eminence; high station (9)
18. An unusually low hooter (3)
20. Labour raised large amount, to which one's contributed (4)
22. Major ski resort (5)
23. Trouble or afflict (3)

Crossword Number 36

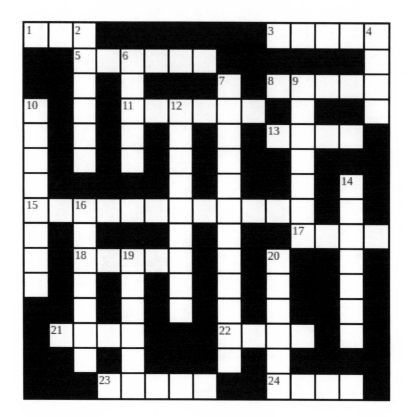

ACROSS

1. Blind part (3)
3. Small top, say (5)
5. Most ready to be picked (6)
8. Snake bite treatment: anti___ (5)
11. Store green fodder (6)
13. Rudolph's dad, e.g. (4)
15. Internal body framework (12)
17. Commencement vip (4)
18. A wicked-o upset for the oil-supplier? (5)
21. Maybe this world is another planet's ___: aldous huxley (4)
22. Firm up the muscles (4)
23. Archaic word for belated (5)
24. Mono attachment (4)

DOWN

2. Having three parts (6)
4. Chinese sleeping-platform (4)
6. Key's comedic partner (5)
7. Racism (12)
9. Indulge artfully in dodging (7)
10. Little poem (8)
12. Serial (9)
14. The - lesson of dr nicolaes tulp; painting by rembrandt (7)
16. Suffocated, in a way medic admitted (7)
19. Roma is its capital (6)
20. A narrowing chimney (6)

Crossword Number 37

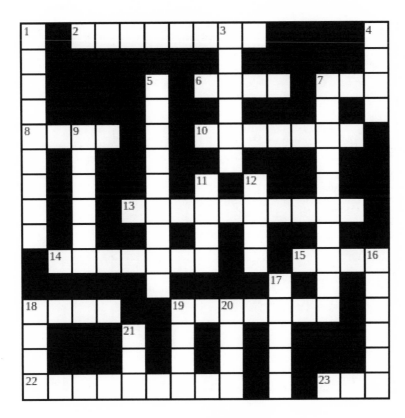

ACROSS

2. Part of book fool's written backwards, puncturing triumph (8)
6. Music industry honors: (abbr.) (4)
7. Acrossfrat letter (3)
8. Hold fast (4)
10. Foot-wart (7)
13. Took (10)
14. ___ entry (7)
15. Quia, quoniam (4)
18. Very happy to make broth (4)
19. Germ-free / barren (7)
22. Mess kit's a pain for citizen of commonwealth (9)
23. Sandwich that's not kosher or vegetarian, for short (3)

DOWN

1. Soldier in very large tanker looking up devotionally (9)
3. German commander called the desert fox (6)
4. Kind of aerial bomb (4)
5. Put (9)
7. Teller of tales broadcast once as true (10)
9. Adapt musically? (6)
11. Type of skink (4)
12. Wary of change that will render one crooked (4)
16. To notice (6)
17. Glycerine start (5)
18. Hold up the post somehow (4)
19. Japanese noodles made from buckwheat flour (4)
20. Case for small articles (4)
21. Detectives, e.g. (3)

Crossword Number 38

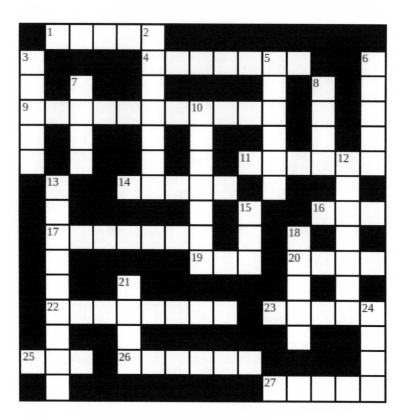

ACROSS

1. Smooth: fr. (5)
4. Government backer, round lunchtime, seen in streets (7)
9. Throwing (11)
11. Top - cow (6)
14. Rejected member that went unheard as a philosopher (5)
16. Wordsmith's offering (3)
17. Doctor bloom at raffle event (7)
19. Brown-capped mushroom (3)
20. The devil's doings (4)
22. Ten past three (8)
23. Tool causing a sudden problem (5)
25. Sound of inebriation (3)
26. Good wet-ground racehorse (6)
27. U.s.s.r. river (5)

DOWN

2. Title placed after name (7)
3. Wild cat of asia (5)
5. Naturally followed (6)
6. Chocolate-coated snack stick (5)
7. Etched, for short (4)
8. Niminy-piminy person (4)
10. Official cocktail of neworleans (7)
12. Eu tried to become scholarly (7)
13. Relating to reflections or mirrors (9)
15. Napoleon's title: (abbr.) (3)
18. Like pizza without meat or real cheese (5)
21. Stiffly formal and precise (person or manner) (4)
24. Welsh resort whose ocean beach funfair closed in 2007 (4)

Crossword Number 39

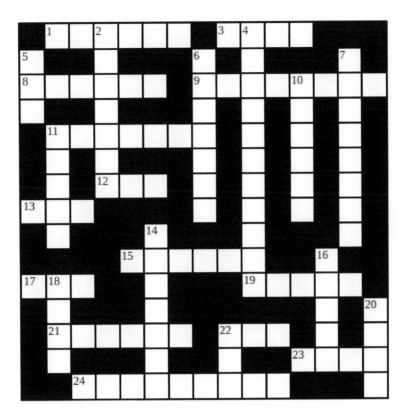

ACROSS

1. Lime ___ (bar drink) (6)
3. Large spiny fish (4)
8. Smartly fashionable (6)
9. Sunk in firmly (8)
11. Effort before the effort (7)
12. Give it your all (3)
13. Winner's gathering (3)
15. Quality of a musical sound as opposed to its pitch and loudness (6)
17. Kazakhstan's largest river (3)
19. New york senator chauncey (5)
21. Extracted information mechanically? (6)
22. Army group under a 39-across (3)
23. That: fr. (4)
24. Seriously puzzled (9)

DOWN

2. Securest (7)
4. Unpaired (11)
5. Defunct chevy convertible truck (3)
6. With a lot of spunk (7)
7. Zeniths (8)
10. Two-masted fishing boat (6)
11. Decorative loop edge for lace/ribbon (5)
14. Surging (7)
16. Shield figure (5)
18. Superstar rapper ___ fiasco (4)
20. Challah unit (4)
22. Defendants of an affair (3)

Crossword Number 40

ACROSS

1. Loosen (up) (5)
5. Sectioned (8)
9. Province of china; capital changsha (5)
10. Head puns? (anag.) (8)
11. Old rr watchdog (3)
12. Membrane of grasses (5)
14. Sam ___,1942 pga championship winner (5)
15. World's most populous country, initially (3)
16. Mote (5)
20. German gets free network (4)
21. Measures engine speed: (abbr.) (4)
22. Like different forms of the same element (8)
23. Slippery in speech (4)

DOWN

2. Restaurant reading matter (5)
3. Graduate celebrated, dropping first ecstasy, and was amazed (9)
4. Promulgating (12)
6. Small specimen moved forward or moved out (5)
7. Gain ulcer, resulting in nervous pain (anag.) (9)
8. Calf meat for cutlets (4)
13. City bank losing capital (3)
14. Major city in pennsylvania, us, on the lackawanna river (8)
15. Fortune-teller kin (7)
17. Curves at the top of a glass (7)
18. A drooping of the upper or lower eyelid (6)
19. Bad, in madrid (4)

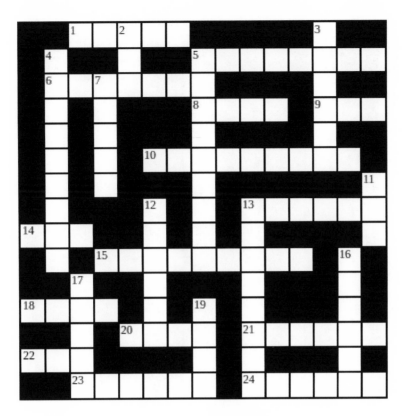

ACROSS

1. Broadly smiling (5)
5. Eel-like creatures (8)
6. Border stitch that is undone at the front (7)
8. Catty reply (4)
9. Actress penelope - miller (3)
10. Refusal (9)
13. Deal with, as a clogged drain (6)
14. July 31st: init. (3)
15. Joke without malice but with some bite (9)
18. Hoppy brews, for short (4)
20. Move on runway cheers team (4)
21. Male gonad (anat.) (6)
22. Look at me, i'm sandra ___ (3)
23. French ww2 resistance (6)
24. Holding device: mech. (6)

DOWN

2. Subj. of tax exemption (3)
3. Games on a particular day could be footy (6)
4. Divvy up (9)
5. Light up (9)
7. Brit's football (5)
11. Word after photo or black (3)
12. It broke up into laurasia and gondwanaland (6)
13. Still to be sampled (8)
16. Restrict the supply of rain to this form of it (6)
17. Road to morocco setting (5)
19. Blown to ___ (exploded) (4)

Crossword Number 42

ACROSS

1. Thrilled (8)
6. Dot-com address: (abbr.) (3)
7. Challenger (8)
12. Oldest breed of duck (7)
13. Paid promotion : (abbr.) (4)
15. Hubble observation (5)
16. M or f (3)
17. Door opening aid (4)
21. Occupancy (11)
23. - milk wood; 1954 radio drama by dylan thomas (5)
24. Corrupting influence (8)

DOWN

2. Actor -kilmer (3)
3. 'how ? want it' (#1 hit for 2pac) (3)
4. Scent (8)
5. Fastener caught up on broken leg (6)
8. Upholding (11)
9. Curriculum ___: resume (5)
10. Indian of the sacramento river valley (4)
11. Industrial centre in germany: little town storing weapons (9)
14. Improve one repair (5)
18. Standard unit of currency of ethiopia (4)
19. French menu choice (6)
20. Snub religious education enthusiast (6)
22. Hawaiian club (3)

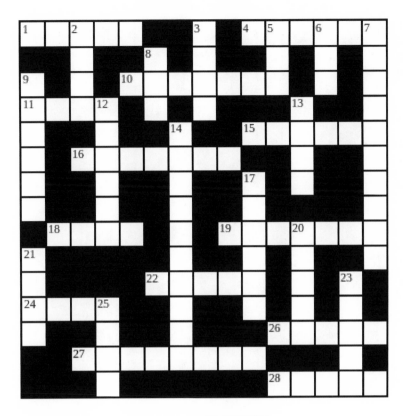

ACROSS

1. One of child's 23 ac (5)
4. City sw of chicago (6)
10. A firmly established sports meeting? (7)
11. Envelop a birthday gift with paper (4)
15. From a bit of old silver, return not fixed (6)
16. Medical case willing to be tolerant (7)
18. Played all game without fielding (4)
19. Still fluster, perhaps (7)
22. Alone, to ovid (5)
24. Greek pastry (4)
26. Employing undergrad to cover up wrong-doing (5)
27. Right woman in group to introduce a piece of music (8)
28. Narrow passage between buildings (5)

DOWN

2. Wall st. (abbr.) (4)
3. Scatterbrained sort (4)
5. Agape, to a bard (3)
6. Online id addresses (3)
7. Steps aren't at all rickety (10)
8. Italian sign language (3)
9. A trick of one speaking for a brief period (6)
12. River paralleled by i-80 through a long stretch of the plains (6)
13. Russian log hut (4)
14. Nerve agent (10)
17. Use any plastic on edge (6)
20. Salad utensils (5)
21. Musical bit (4)
23. So there will be sun - nice out (5)
25. Pay attention, you down under! (4)

Crossword Number 44

ACROSS

1. Predicted cut following warning (7)
4. Book's foreword: (abbr.) (4)
5. Local model about to quote me in provocation (10)
8. King of the huns who devastated much of the roman empire (6)
12. Most charming copper on trial (6)
13. Strip the chaos of ruin with gravity (5)
15. Razorbill is of this genus (4)
16. Oversupplies (10)
19. Indiana jones codirector (5)
20. Cunningly, in a silly way! (5)
22. Near lake, in distress (7)
23. Chinese wellness practice (6)

DOWN

1. Lie about republican wrangling (8)
2. Agcy. seeking aliens (4)
3. Small axe (7)
6. Devastating (10)
7. Inner chamber of ancient greek temple (4)
9. Part of o.t. (4)
10. A number also being worried about multiple firings (5)
11. Objects from everyday life (6)
14. Roman coins that india re-issued (7)
17. Seasoned food served up in lima - lashings! (6)
18. Feeling down in the dumps (4)
21. Go at a medium pace on a treadmill (3)

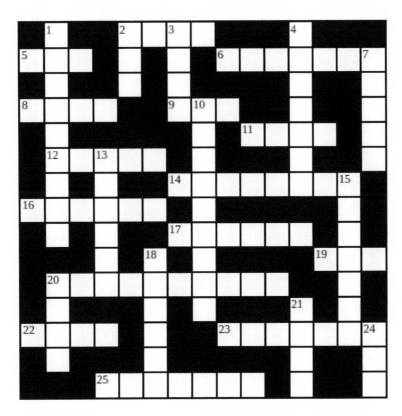

ACROSS

2. Go back having left dairy product in tent (4)
5. It's concerned with national security in the states [acronym] (3)
6. Did (7)
8. Archaic conjugation of 'be' (4)
9. Will.i.am's bandmate, ___.de.ap (3)
11. Bright red not allowed in mark from wound (4)
12. Spherical bacteria (5)
14. Most amusing (8)
16. Discount graduate in tree management (6)
17. Less-traveled way (6)
19. Horizontal opp. (3)
20. Decided a month back he for one was to lead (10)
22. Class of '96 member (4)
23. Unnatural sounding and overformal (7)
25. Following orders (7)

DOWN

1. Zips (9)
2. Smallest letter of hebrew alphabet (3)
3. Egyptian solar deity and mother deity (4)
4. Traveller's suitcases and bags (7)
7. Below normal size (5)
10. Tranquilizing (9)
13. Half a magician's incantation (6)
15. Theatrical roman playing centre back for internazionale (7)
18. Irregular bounce of small ball (6)
20. N.m. indian (4)
21. Work hard and steadily at something (4)
24. Abbreviation for dar es salaam (3)

Crossword Number 46

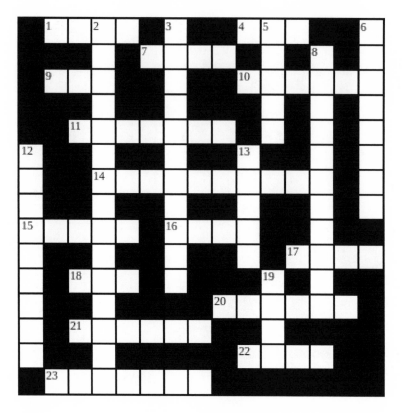

ACROSS

1. Who? you're able (4)
4. Hyundai santa fe, for one: (abbr.) (3)
7. Fellow has to go on runs (4)
9. ___ punk: no doubt genre (3)
10. A hard mineral (6)
11. Like a young lassie (7)
14. Darkness (10)
15. Christianity, e.g.: (abbr.) (5)
16. Romeo et juliette segment (4)
17. Call for a band (4)
18. Article for helmut (3)
20. Sea with a unifying idea (6)
21. Investor's profit (6)
22. Liquidy lump (inf) (4)
23. Refuse to take orders (7)

DOWN

2. Imagination (15)
3. Freon, for one (11)
5. Allow to float, as a currency's price (5)
6. Element, se its symbol (8)
8. Child killing (11)
12. Tarnishing (9)
13. Threshold (psychol.) (5)
19. Securely close up a marine carnivore (4)

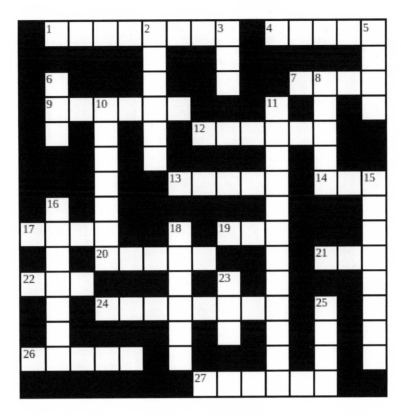

ACROSS

1. Anne of tv's topper (8)
4. Like 11-down's walls (5)
7. Biblical verb (4)
9. Gorsuch's predecessor (6)
12. ___ brothers pictures (6)
13. Yankees manager aaron (5)
14. Rain coat from rugby (3)
17. Black liquid to turn into vapour (4)
19. Latin diphthongs (3)
20. Mouth-part i'd found in fatty tissue (5)
21. Shut-eye (3)
22. Solo with a wookiee co-pilot (3)
24. Olden people (8)
26. Stressed syllable in verse (5)
27. Within a deadline (6)

DOWN

2. Broccoli-like vegetable (6)
3. Beach lotion's (3)
5. Half-rotten (4)
6. Writer mr. eliot, et al. (3)
8. James ___ garfield (5)
10. Happy (7)
11. Thin (12)
15. Made barrels (8)
16. Sea or space traveller (7)
18. Assessing magnitude (6)
23. Ethyl or carot follower (3)
25. Loco, when repeated (4)

Crossword Number 48

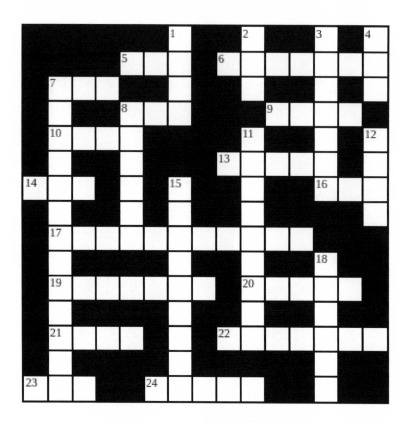

ACROSS

5. Least populous state: (abbr.) (3)
6. Tool used in some deliveries (7)
7. ___ indianapolis (3)
8. Try to satisfy your curiosity (3)
9. Kumar, comedian (4)
10. Dime e.g. (4)
13. Hen, to henri (5)
14. Caloric meas. (3)
16. Fiber clusters in wool (3)
17. Vaulting (11)
19. Aspen shaking head of bog myrtle (7)
20. Computer email folder (5)
21. Emulate a logger (4)
22. Extreme self-conceit (7)
23. Say it to agree (3)
24. Rut cut in from left (5)

DOWN

1. Barnes & noble purchase (4)
2. Place to park outside a mall (3)
3. China seems in turmoil (7)
4. Missile initials (3)
7. Not commodious or easeful (13)
8. One seeking haul from bank? (6)
11. Rewriting (9)
12. 1980 nfl mvp brian (4)
15. Too big? old hem covers most of fat (9)
18. European - might be french (6)

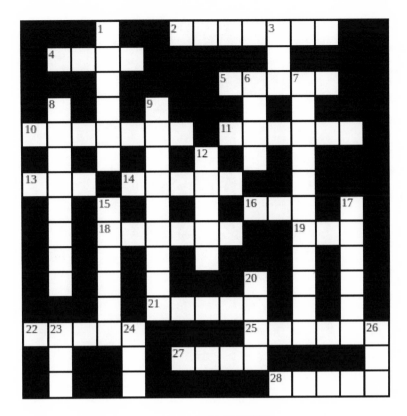

ACROSS

2. Tastes (7)
4. Large-handled items used for chopping (4)
5. Freight (5)
10. Washing (7)
11. Salad ingredient, excessively dull when eaten (6)
13. Teacher's deg. (3)
14. Exclude beard (5)
16. ___ grass (meadow barley) (3)
18. Travelled faster (6)
19. Anc country (3)
21. Like ___, all tears: hamlet (5)
22. Ending for snub (5)
25. Sea with a unifying idea (6)
27. Site of a biblical wedding (4)
28. Fruit mostly for ape (5)

DOWN

1. Chap engaged in ogling? not half (6)
3. Impressive looking vase (3)
6. Old testament book between joel and obadiah (4)
7. Edible woodland mushroom (11)
8. Feature of namibia and libya (8)
9. Not sure or confident (9)
12. Belfast river (5)
15. Rapidly changing crowd attached to the italian quarter (6)
17. Ornamental arm band (6)
20. Sixth letter out of 24 (4)
23. Horrific tolkien beast (3)
24. Worked on (3)
26. ___ hit'an of alaska (3)

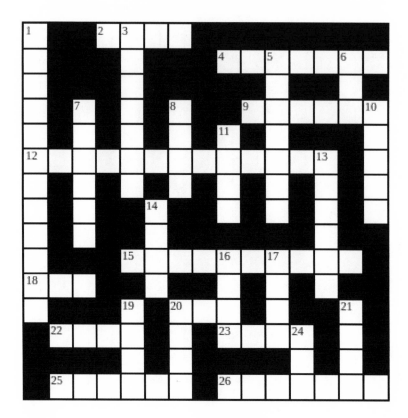

ACROSS

2. Russian city on the ural (4)
4. Fragrant asian rice (7)
9. Excrement (6)
12. Make salable (13)
15. South dublin district (10)
18. Rcmp patrol place, briefly (3)
20. Goat call (3)
22. Home of triple-a baseball's aces (4)
23. One of the overheads for a gangster (4)
25. Saw off the tongue (6)
26. Parodist (7)

DOWN

1. Vowing (12)
3. Made a recovery (7)
5. Show soldiers around if in a state (7)
6. Burmese demon (3)
7. A moron's confused? hard cheese! (6)
8. A little (in music) (4)
10. ___ day (tree-planting holiday) (5)
11. Feeds the goats, perhaps (4)
13. Drink, say, going up? i cleared off! (6)
14. Rumpelstiltskin's weaver (4)
16. Informal yes (4)
17. Plumbing specialists company, ___-rooter (4)
19. 10 cutting leg without gold sandal (4)
20. Econ. major's course (4)
21. Icicle place (4)
24. 1957 physics nobelist tsung-___ lee (3)

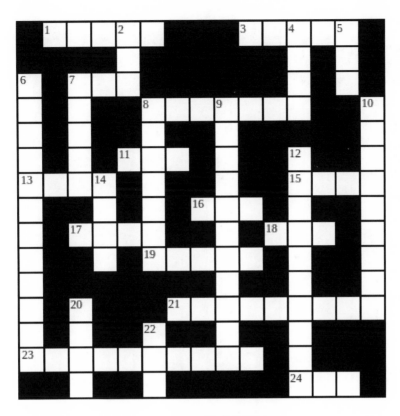

ACROSS

1. Rock singer hagar (5)
3. Thief's unpleasant to an australian (5)
7. Dog show initials (3)
8. British banking name (7)
11. Scriptural ed. (3)
13. Language of west-central nigeria (4)
15. Party hat's shape (4)
16. Journalists brought about change in n korea (3)
17. Thunder star, familiarly (4)
18. Irish dance (3)
19. Battery acid spilt on end of piston (5)
21. Determinable (9)
23. Very large ham (10)
24. Conference gp. (3)

DOWN

2. Como, familiarly (3)
4. Wise to reject vinyl worth a small amount (4)
5. Longtime cia rival (3)
6. Checked (12)
7. Take ___ (vacation) (5)
8. Obtains different defence (7)
9. Weighty (11)
10. Not again (poetical) (9)
12. Tilted (10)
14. Abbreviation for emergency (4)
20. Finish stone work (4)
22. Pilgrimage centre instigating quotas on mecca (3)

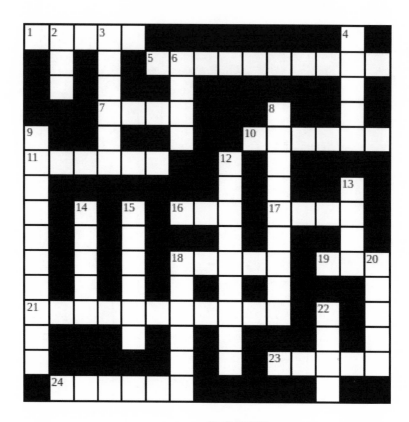

ACROSS

1. Orange ___ : refreshing drink (5)
5. Not dependent (10)
7. Actress ms blanchett (4)
10. Writing or entering (6)
11. Everyone stays at home? object (6)
16. One type of tv screen (3)
17. Rice like grains of pasta (4)
18. Was confusing to the leathernecks to crowd so densely (5)
19. Aren't ___ fine pair of misfits? (3)
21. Large company (11)
23. Protection for a front door (5)
24. Give approval to rat, if i say so (6)

DOWN

2. Ones, in weedon (3)
3. Translucent cover for plants (6)
4. Confine, obstruct (5)
6. Votes against hooter being sounded (4)
8. No romcoms set in this part of ireland (9)
9. He makes acquaintances (10)
12. Takeing (9)
13. Sitcom, ___ mothers do 'ave 'em (4)
14. More verifiable (5)
15. Boys and girls, informally (6)
18. Covered with sores (6)
20. On ___ (exulting) (5)
22. Persephone (4)

Crossword Number 53

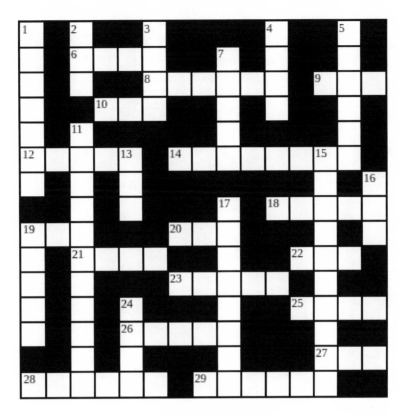

ACROSS

6. Leaf/stem angle (4)
8. Darner (anag.) (6)
9. Grand ___ (wine making phrase) (3)
10. Cut grass on a lawn (3)
12. Lawbreaker gets shepherd's staff (5)
14. More sordid (8)
18. Hidden under muscular flap i had fatty stuff (5)
19. Cook sausages (3)
20. Summer bay fit is an example of one of these (3)
21. Christmas sometimes involves a church service (4)
22. Mr. robbins (3)
23. Item of playground equipment (5)
25. Dubya's veep (4)
26. Copy more profitable sandwiches (5)
27. Make a touchdown (3)
28. Old-fashioned people (6)
29. Like baking dough (6)

DOWN

1. Carp and turkey with cream (7)
2. Chan marshall, aka ___ power (3)
3. One ___ over the cuckoo's nest, 1975 jack nicholson film (4)
4. Area ___; threedigit number (4)
5. Simple kind of economy (6)
7. Rock to sleep, say (5)
11. Wellpaying (11)
13. Tool assortment (3)
15. Specifically (10)
16. Lettered pre-smartphone device (3)
17. One who eats everything wasted more vino (8)
19. Some dogs (5)
24. Semi-domesticated fish found in poor fettle (4)

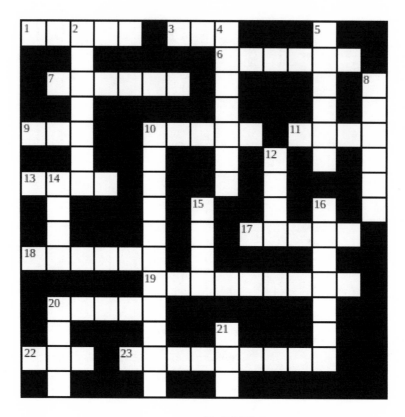

ACROSS

1. Messy, disgusting (5)
3. 'tis a pity sound (3)
6. Continual complainant (6)
7. N.b.a. hall-of-famer bob (6)
9. Terse response to "where are you going?" (3)
10. Matter that is neither gas nor liquid (5)
11. Of the church of england: (abbr.) (4)
13. Spinal membrane (4)
17. Gaelic cry of grief (5)
18. One who apprehends (6)
19. Means somehow secured to be given an 18 (9)
20. Pepper holder? (5)
22. Cousin of an adv. (3)
23. Curled (9)

DOWN

2. Loud rattling noise (7)
4. Astute ruler seen around at present (7)
5. Civil war historian allan (6)
8. Big, awkward one (6)
10. Matter (11)
12. Indonesian seaport (4)
14. Sky: comb. form (4)
15. Capital of osterreich (4)
16. Zipped (7)
20. Spock's rank: (abbr.) (4)
21. Sentimental tattoo (3)

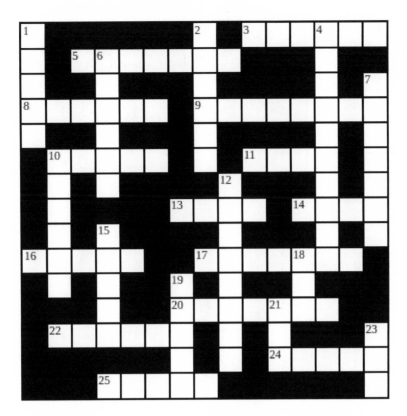

ACROSS

3. Cello bottom (6)
5. Pulitzer prize biographer (7)
8. World's third largest ocean (6)
9. Promote too strongly (8)
10. Quiet for a gun they say (5)
11. Bunch of wool in carpet futuristic backing will reveal (4)
13. Student in wager to sing loudly (4)
14. Latin for see (4)
16. Uplifted? not one that's totally devastated (5)
17. Start off from exchange in london area (7)
20. Alas! our problem is excitement (7)
22. Night author elie (6)
24. Lover's cross singer (5)
25. 1998 action film starring robert de niro and jean reno (5)

DOWN

1. Norse god of the sea (5)
2. Guttenberg film (6)
4. Son occupying newly repainted flat (10)
6. Pertaining to funeral ceremonies (6)
7. Piano, to mozart (7)
10. Old-style hacker (6)
12. Random beer with a conservative (8)
15. For this reason . (5)
18. Frigate bird of hawaii (3)
19. Lobsters' sense organs (5)
21. Baglike cavity enclosed by a membrane in an animal or plant (3)
23. Give ___ call (3)

ACROSS

1. Flutist jean-pierre (6)
3. Trouble, in yiddish (6)
7. 1944 historical romance novel by kathleen winsor (5)
8. Limb-bending muscle (6)
13. Roosevelt cabinet member (5)
14. Seat of power, then or new (6)
15. Grain-eating bug (6)
17. Decided (upon course of action) (8)
21. Dragon prince fantasy series author melanie (4)
23. Small watery channel (4)
24. Superficial or slight (7)
26. Show noted tennis player getting up infused with energy (6)

DOWN

2. Jetty, as in fuchsia 'wigan ___' (4)
4. Refer legal case about british museum (6)
5. Bringing about (7)
6. King mackerel (4)
9. And about to prop things up if beached (7)
10. Give out smoke (4)
11. Rescue last of fine offal placed in skip (11)
12. Bubbling away (5)
16. One who bewilders (7)
18. Beth ___, lead singer of gossip (5)
19. Frighteningly odd, spelled oddly (4)
20. Ak, once (4)
22. Us president eisenhower's nickname (3)
25. ___ up (old-style perturbed) (3)

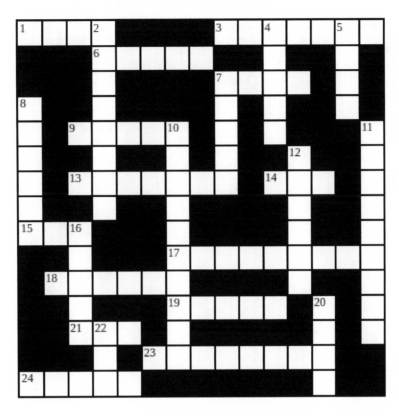

ACROSS

1. Rush away (4)
3. Tiger salamander's cousin (7)
6. Diplomatic representative (5)
7. Dispute decider, at times (4)
9. Transmission-related units (5)
13. Star's path originally followed by sailor adrift (7)
14. Apt. feature, in ads (3)
15. They oversee the grand canyon: (abbr.) (3)
17. Car lamp (9)
18. Tryst twosome (6)
19. Where iloilo is (5)
21. Golfer -alcott (3)
23. Nitroglycerine explosive (8)
24. Unclean (5)

DOWN

2. Could he be described as self-willed? (8)
4. Post a comment on a political blog, say (5)
5. Crime fiction characters (4)
7. Order a form (5)
8. Pollen-producer (6)
10. Scot. country dance (10)
11. Simulating moving (9)
12. Point (weapon) wrongly (6)
16. Roman dress (5)
20. Became a competitor (4)
22. 1970 novel by peter tinniswood (3)

Crossword Number 58

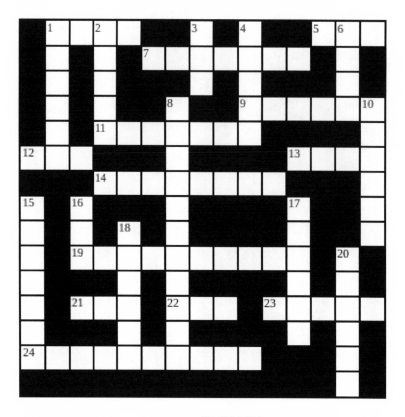

ACROSS

1. Ancient city in south america (4)
5. Cecil ___ mille (3)
7. Study of mapping mountains (7)
9. Values customer, it seems, in part (6)
11. Financial matters (7)
12. Like two beethoven symphonies (3)
13. Infrequently found (4)
14. In a limited manner (8)
19. Fastidious attitude of one city poser (10)
21. Marked (a ballot) (3)
22. Laughlin in tex., e.g. (3)
23. Beam is splitting a bit (5)
24. Collaborate (10)

DOWN

1. Not marked by levity (6)
2. 2011 drama starring michael fassbender and carey mulligan (5)
3. Vertical opposite, for short (3)
4. See girl covered in soil? (5)
6. Wipe with a dry cloth (4)
8. Beneficial substance in foods (11)
10. Santa's the back of (6)
15. Belonging to a threesome (7)
16. ___-huggers (type of pants) (3)
17. Passionflower fruit (6)
18. Dutch university town (6)
20. Fairly scorching at first, temperature in summer month (6)

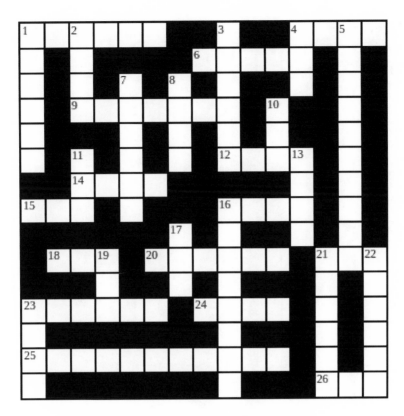

ACROSS

1. Fairly scorching at first, temperature in summer month (6)
4. An ogre (4)
6. The chief monetary unit of poland (5)
9. County to w of dublin (7)
12. Daniel of comedy central (4)
14. Silver coin of ancient greece worth one sixth of a drachma (4)
15. Hockey-team complement (3)
16. Playboy of yesteryear (4)
18. British poet, henry james ___ (b.1744 - d.1813) (3)
20. Runner on the stairs (6)
21. Unite in ritual (3)
23. Optics (6)
24. The americans star ___ russell (4)
25. Greed (11)
26. 'not -' (3)

DOWN

1. Spoke humorously (6)
2. Vancouver-born broadcaster, ___-yin lee (4)
3. Flowing smoothly (6)
4. Seed's reward (3)
5. Raw material for nuclear reactors (10)
7. Air force pilot, in slang (6)
8. Requiem, e.g. (4)
10. Nasa's six-person orbiter (3)
11. Hamstring (3)
13. Section of the editorial meriting attention (4)
16. Lowered oneself via rope (8)
17. Multiple activation key: (abbr.) (3)
19. Martin luther opponent johann (3)
21. Easily handled or used (6)
22. Leave the station (6)
23. Wife upset pet and broke down (4)

Crossword Number 60

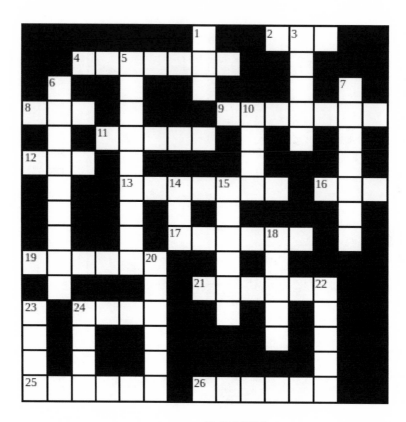

ACROSS

2. Fourth tones in scales (3)
4. Cricketer seen if climbing tree (7)
8. Helicopter hero's (abbr.) (3)
9. Unmanageable horses, in the southwest (7)
11. Word with minted (5)
12. Packaged army food [acronym] (3)
13. Fell with dull, heavy sound (7)
16. Software release no. (3)
17. Period when a computer is working (6)
19. A race to finish - be there! (6)
21. Violent twist or pull (6)
24. Hummus holders (4)
25. How the waitress said only pie for dessert? (6)
26. Part of toga the romans put in pleats (6)

DOWN

1. He lost to dde twice (3)
3. Upbeat, in music terminology (5)
5. Freak, not counting overs in nets (9)
6. Old german forced to go short (9)
7. Colony of birds or seals (7)
10. Shaft in a drivetrain (4)
14. Inuit hunter's gadget (3)
15. Cardinal's office (6)
18. Like some strays (5)
20. Discover code's cryptic in part (6)
22. Present with a blue ribbon, say (5)
23. Where to apply compound w (4)
24. 1983 racehorse film, - lap (4)

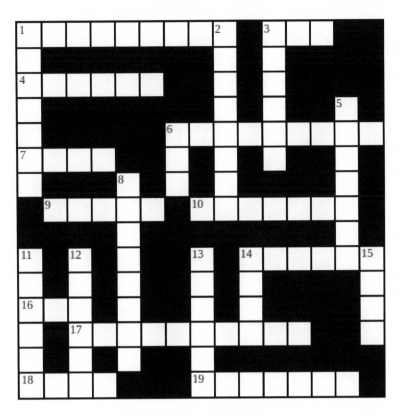

ACROSS

1. Wholesomenesses (9)
3. Vixen (3)
4. Eyeing greedily (6)
6. Umbrella bead (9)
7. The bird of paradise (4)
9. Survives terrible evils (5)
10. Asphyxiation without satin creates lack of oxygen (7)
14. Sank, subsided (6)
16. Hemic trio (3)
17. Whole (10)
18. Grate thin slices of potato with no skin (4)
19. Like some german wines (7)

DOWN

1. Ticket taker (7)
2. Refining center (8)
3. Physical shape or form (6)
5. Produce leaves (7)
6. Ruby, it seems, softens when warmed up (3)
8. Vocal trio (8)
11. Thermographic camera, e.g. (6)
12. Oxford first in even game (6)
13. Stealer of goods (6)
14. 10 1/2 wide, e.g. (4)
15. Ding in a door (4)

Crossword Number 62

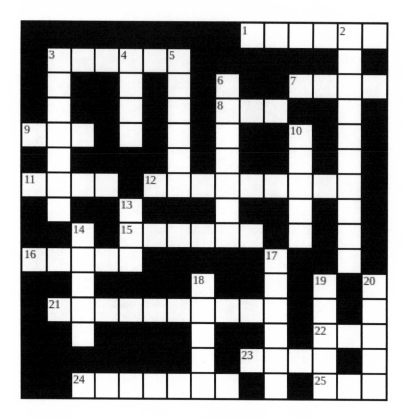

ACROSS

1. Towboat (6)
3. Yielding (6)
7. Castle chess piece (4)
8. Batteries for digital cameras (3)
9. Cecil ___ mille (3)
11. Communist founder (4)
12. Hypodermic fluid (9)
15. Needlework in corner of large house? (6)
16. Rush of seawater (5)
21. Is he stranded in mid-air? (10)
22. Currency unit of 18 down (3)
23. Big particle physics lab in switz. (4)
24. Sung, as in the swiss alps (7)
25. E-mail writer, e.g.: (abbr.) (3)

DOWN

2. Lengthening (10)
3. Oprah companion ___ graham (7)
4. Virginia willow genus (4)
5. Neighbor of new london (6)
6. Vessel with another following current coming to holy residence (7)
10. Make self conscious (5)
13. Bit of soot (3)
14. Card game (5)
17. Boston mayor james (6)
18. European kite (5)
19. Mathematician ___ turing, and others (5)
20. Leading and respected citizen (5)

Crossword Number 63

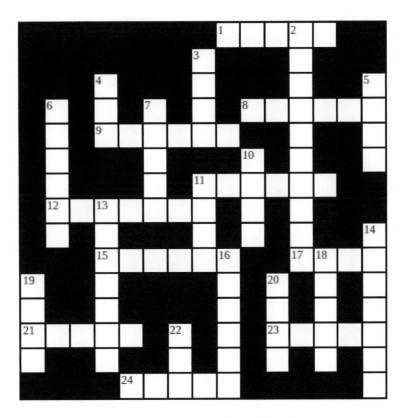

ACROSS

1. Common scapegoat (5)
8. Apologetic (6)
9. Farthest from the center, in anatomy (6)
11. Not forming an angle (6)
12. Yiddish jerks (7)
15. Printing press handle (6)
17. For once it's the puzzler's answer (4)
21. Extra, briefly (5)
23. ___ facie (legal phrase) (5)
24. Port and former capital of nigeria on the bight of benin (5)

DOWN

2. Insect flutters if one gets caught how biologist's described? (10)
3. ___ mater (alumnus' school) (4)
4. Letter of the hebrew alphabet (3)
5. Play a tuba or trumpet (4)
6. Shaft by which air leaves a mine; sap cut (anag.) (6)
7. Filipino dish (5)
10. Scrape by (4)
11. Application specific integrated circuit (4)
13. Nosing (7)
14. Third tone of a scale (7)
16. Heat condition (6)
18. Certain antibody (5)
19. Bring up this kind of guard (4)
20. Hip-hop's ___ fiasco (4)
22. Abrupt turn (3)

Crossword Number 64

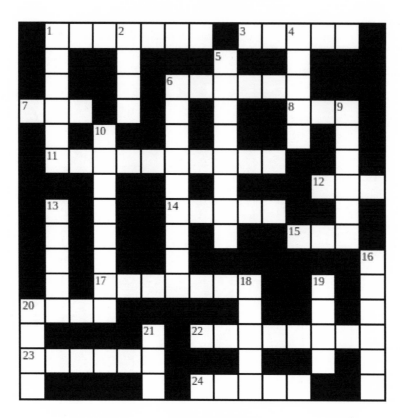

ACROSS

1. Kind of dog bed found in street on the outskirts of ilfracombe (7)
3. Us storyteller remus, perhaps, penning author's introduction (5)
6. Persuade by threats (6)
7. Sound from a squeaky toy (3)
8. Insolent option to sir (3)
11. Lyrists, men out to offer musical performance (10)
12. Lacking in brilliance, brightness or lustre (3)
14. Your table is ready device, often (5)
15. It might follow lemon (3)
17. Drains (7)
20. There's some lack of coherence in this area (4)
22. Resemble mother-of-pearl (8)
23. Fatty; resembling fat (6)
24. Woman with magical power (5)

DOWN

1. One branch of islam (6)
2. Part of a gillette razor name (4)
4. Single-celled organism (var.) (5)
5. Blood bank science (8)
6. Kneading (9)
9. Serbia (anag.) (6)
10. Settle firmly (8)
13. Perfume ceremonially (5)
16. Under ___; not acting freely (6)
18. Chuck out wild civet (5)
19. Reply to, for short (4)
20. Den of an otter; or, a word for an area of woodland (4)
21. Sharable file format (3)

Crossword Number 65

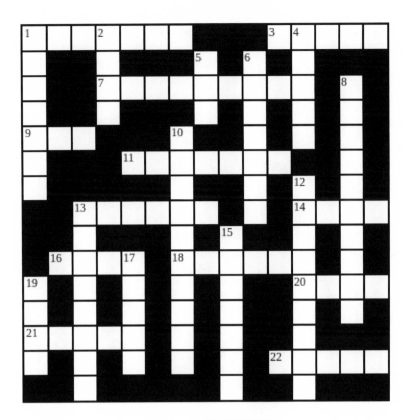

ACROSS

1. Consisting of birch wood (7)
3. Pent up in a pigpen (5)
7. Big rise? cleaner's put in for extra payment (9)
9. When s.n.l. wraps in n.y.c. (3)
11. Certain clothier (7)
13. Like an adonis, in slang (6)
14. Book before daniel: (abbr.) (4)
16. Give kudos (4)
18. Church gets two rings from two quarters to pick from (6)
20. French sky (4)
21. Protagonist of the twilight books (5)
22. Poor golf shots (5)

DOWN

1. Checkout lines (7)
2. Toronto's majestic attraction, ___ loma (4)
4. Man in drag who was enthralled (5)
5. Clergyman's deg. (3)
6. Quick to accept side's leadership (7)
8. Expounded (10)
10. Very lively and amusing lecture (10)
12. Pick boundaries for lake district environs (9)
13. Regularly billed in hoaxes to create confusion (8)
15. Small whale with beak-like snout (7)
17. Sticker (5)
19. The game of marbles (4)

Crossword Number 66

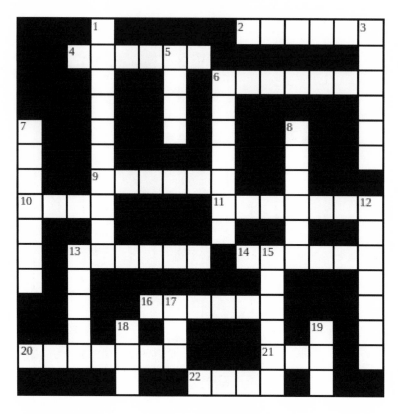

ACROSS

2. Point (weapon) wrongly (6)
4. Unacceptable to entertain independent thought (6)
6. The rig's adjusted for test firing (7)
9. Sound of instrument gives sign (6)
10. Extra weight allowance (4)
11. Interweave; intertwine (7)
13. Texas river (6)
14. Thorough medical examination (6)
16. Laboured (6)
20. Just one detroit hockey player: 2 wds. (7)
21. Us body advocating gun rights (3)
22. One-named body-image advocate (4)

DOWN

1. Conceited hustler (anag.) (10)
3. Spoiled, impaired (6)
5. Take - loan (borrow cash) (4)
6. Dance when joined by ms ballas on strictly (7)
7. Manhattan area (7)
8. Street lender of great interest (6)
12. Region of northern europe (7)
13. Rifle shooter's aid (5)
15. Giraudoux play (6)
17. Support stage for journey (3)
18. Us treasury title: (abbr.) (3)
19. Lumber mill tool (3)

Crossword Number 67

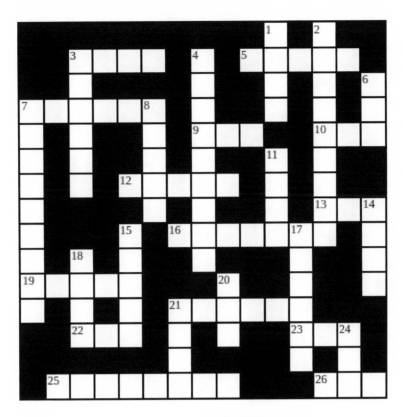

ACROSS

3. Nursery rhyme, oldking... (4)
5. Author of the wretched of the earth (5)
7. Edible, old-style (6)
9. It often lasts for years (3)
10. Undecided, on a sched. (3)
12. Scene of contest in paris (5)
13. Weird al's cult movie (3)
16. Greek antique (7)
19. River herrings (5)
21. Device for, eg, cutting eggs (6)
22. Apocrypha book: (abbr.) (3)
23. You give cheek with this? (3)
25. Promise man bread with this starter (8)
26. Initials-sharers of rush's drummer (3)

DOWN

1. Acidic in taste (4)
2. Polite european with nothing entered tennis area with us (9)
3. Carver's tool (6)
4. Sort of leave ward and dress (9)
6. Mason's stand by (3)
7. Of, by or typical of an author (9)
8. Outlying residentialarea (5)
11. An act in variety theatre will go off like the milk (4)
14. Spinning fixtures on ceilings (4)
15. Ancient poet of scandinavia (5)
17. Empty valise found in airport? that's too much! (6)
18. Made a rug, perhaps (4)
20. Bookie's charge (u.s. slang) (3)
21. Vowel sound (4)
24. Great expectations character (3)

Crossword Number 68

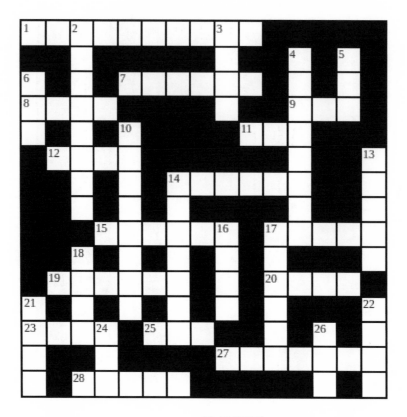

ACROSS

1. One paid to be copied (10)
7. Showed around in escort on back road? (6)
8. Bedouin leader (4)
9. Aphid food (3)
11. Camper's snoozing spot (3)
12. St. john's ___. airport (4)
14. Strike-throwing pitcher (6)
15. Not out much? that's private (6)
17. Courage born out of, (just quietly), good fortune (5)
19. Name on rio bank notes (6)
20. Raised symbol of resistance (4)
23. Townsmen (4)
25. Some securities: (abbr.) (3)
27. Andrew ___, english metaphysical poet (7)
28. Cases to keep needles and thread (5)

DOWN

2. Character of a place (8)
3. Jewish pre-holiday eve (4)
4. Exam no longer held in the country (8)
5. Jagmeet singh's party (3)
6. Spoken form of the letter z (3)
10. Sullen face (8)
13. Us president put on gangster's uniform (5)
14. Goofed, in golf (7)
16. Wireless pioneer (4)
17. Peru's mad, importing very loud locomotive (6)
18. Dirt (4)
21. Canadian mil. org (4)
22. Pyeongchang 2018 winter olympics! skier's support, just one here (4)
24. What was said to boxer in depositions (3)
26. Stud on shoe regularly caught in sleigh (3)

Crossword Number 69

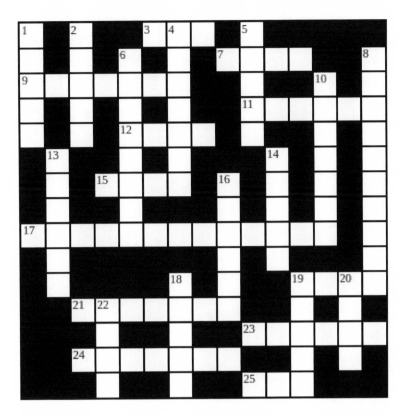

ACROSS

3. Mil. force (3)
7. Nursery rhyme, oldking... (4)
9. Pirate's reportedly crude song (7)
11. In can (6)
12. Theatrical sigh (4)
15. When many eat lunch (4)
17. Unintelligence (13)
19. And middle western sheep (4)
21. Protective barrier put round post office by english pm (7)
23. Improperly divert (money etc) (6)
24. Black-footed albatrosses (7)
25. Old sitcom the doris ___ show (3)

DOWN

1. Red herring (5)
2. Dormouse (5)
4. Railroad yard building (7)
5. Covered with or blackened by soot (5)
6. Follow goal with a gnt cocktail (8)
8. Unions (10)
10. Difficult individual to wake? not entirely (7)
13. Certain facial blemish (6)
14. Torn (5)
16. Sell or hawk (6)
18. Not drunk when sedate and rational (5)
19. Multilane rte. (5)
20. Workplace fairness agcy. (4)
22. Macao money (4)

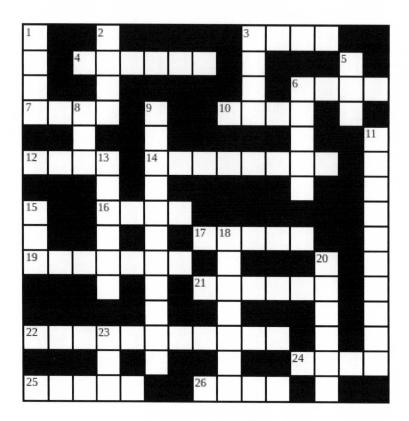

ACROSS

3. Sea ___ (five-armed creature) (4)
4. Sent an overseas telegram to (6)
6. Kill intentionally (4)
7. Very light brown color (4)
10. Hammerin' ___ aaron (4)
12. Floating mass of weeds on white nile (4)
14. Divine (8)
16. Fore of a ship (4)
17. Ukrainian leaping dance (5)
19. Thermal spring (7)
21. Series of ten (6)
22. Impeaching (11)
24. Master copy, for short (4)
25. Group of unmissable, up-and-coming singers (5)
26. Colored, as grey hair (4)

DOWN

1. The elbe, to a czech (4)
2. Deerlike african mouse (4)
3. Egyptian oasis (4)
5. Initially a pensioner (3)
6. U2 window in the ___ (5)
8. ___ dwarf, sci-fi comedy series (3)
9. Sultry (11)
11. Crowning (10)
13. Fraud (6)
15. President taft's monogram (3)
18. Unhealthy fatness (7)
20. Back kelvin to defend mike's comment (6)
23. Rap, reggae, or rock: (abbr.) (3)

Crossword Number 71

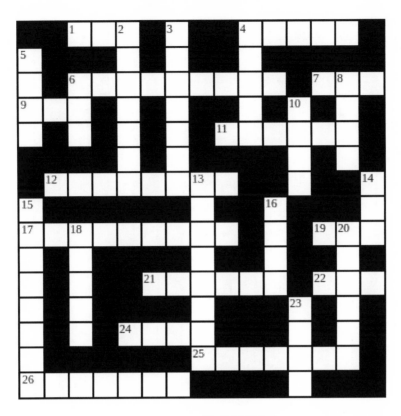

ACROSS

1. It's torture for college employee (3)
4. Wrestling singlet material (5)
6. Preventing from speaking (9)
7. Australian state, briefly (3)
9. Big shot seen in annual reports (3)
11. They line the river (6)
12. Man with two wives (8)
17. Restore to harmony (9)
19. Military abbr. on a beatles album (3)
21. King of arms, and not christian name (6)
22. Tool assortment (3)
24. Casablanca (4)
25. More fashionable, in britain (7)
26. Harden (7)

DOWN

2. Flourishing artist depicts ancient city of syria (7)
3. Indian turned up, shot in ulster (7)
4. Long wooden spear (5)
5. Focuses of power (4)
6. Garden center roll (3)
8. Weed clogging white nile (4)
10. Trademark (abbr.) (4)
13. Period in which early invertebrate land animals appeared (8)
14. Revolver or other firearm (3)
15. Extremely unhappy (8)
16. Over-optimistic, wordy, lacking power (4)
18. Trouble for tomb raiders (5)
20. Kvetch (6)
23. Agitate, mix (4)

Crossword Number 72

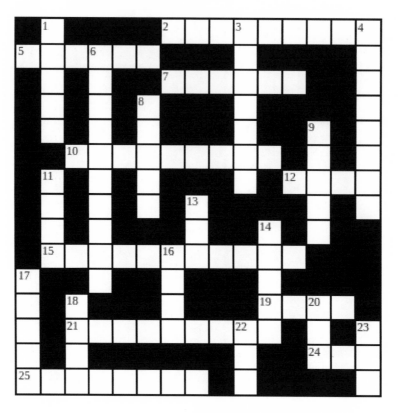

ACROSS

2. Glided with plane motor cut off (9)
5. Transmitter of motion from camshaft to valve (6)
7. Without any others being included (6)
10. Linking together (9)
12. Self-operating napkin creator goldberg (4)
15. Inclined to short attacks of drowsiness (11)
19. Sunrise direccion (4)
21. So monarch not in immediate danger? that's not yet confirmed (9)
24. What novels begin as: (abbr.) (3)
25. Nearer the front? move into rear (8)

DOWN

1. Striped (cat) (5)
3. Hunting, as for food (7)
4. Doomed, but isn't upset during action (8)
6. Point of card game, not on line - employing memory (10)
8. Native of tashkent (5)
9. Urarthritic (5)
11. ___ of kachchh (4)
13. Fruit picker in genesis (3)
14. A biased argument is one (5)
16. Elegance, french style (4)
17. Striped mammal (5)
18. Go back having left dairy product in tent (4)
20. Cruise around hollywood solution in next week's classifieds (3)
22. Knoxville-tod.c. dir. (3)
23. Ene's reverse (3)

Crossword Number 73

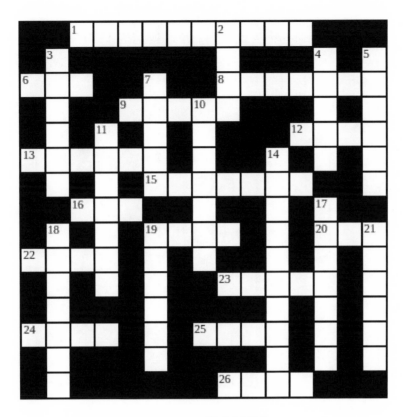

ACROSS

1. Ongoing parking trouble in streets (10)
6. The man that can be heard in church song (3)
8. Prehistoric southwest culture (7)
9. Did some cutting and kept the blades short! (5)
12. A sharply directional antenna (4)
13. Lace alternative on running shoes (6)
15. With few details (7)
16. Blog feed format letters (3)
19. Short notice means little appreciation (4)
20. And cry with alarm (3)
22. Lead-in to -drome (4)
23. Sneaker bottom's pattern (5)
24. Trifle with dessert (4)
25. Residential area, e.g. (4)
26. Bear dance participants (4)

DOWN

2. Classical : (abbr.) (4)
3. Having a lip (6)
4. Related to 25-across (5)
5. More astute of huw ultimately to remain in ireland (6)
7. Ancient greek province (5)
10. Peaceful country, but not quite pleasant (7)
11. Carved cross is cut in a particular style (7)
14. Worthwhile (10)
17. Pissedoff (7)
18. Sherman's dog in rocky & bullwinkle, mr ___ (7)
19. Car document; ticket book (6)
21. Early communist set, occupying hideouts, dismissing leader (6)

Crossword Number 74

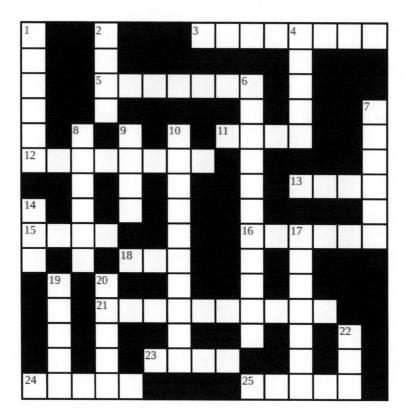

ACROSS

3. Tinted feature of some cars (8)
5. Soft fabric (7)
11. Miller's son gets great deal (4)
12. Scoffing second cereal, almost replete (8)
13. Well-known speaker (4)
15. Classic 1970s tv period drama series, ___ the boat comes in (4)
16. Ancient egyptian coin (6)
18. Hour bit, in brief (3)
21. Rag committee are involved with packaging (10)
23. One thousandth of a second. (4)
24. Japanese-style fencing (5)
25. Helped, briefly (5)

DOWN

1. A real pain in the ear (6)
2. Containing double entendres, say (4)
4. Scottish teams air crash at heathrow central (5)
6. Mayflower starting port (11)
7. South african hot spot of 1976 (6)
8. Parrots and one rook escaping from hgvs (6)
9. Oldfashioned preposition (4)
10. Worried (10)
14. Plant tassel (3)
17. Milk producers (7)
19. Measure fruit round prune's middle (5)
20. Going rate (5)
22. Adj. for some stock (3)

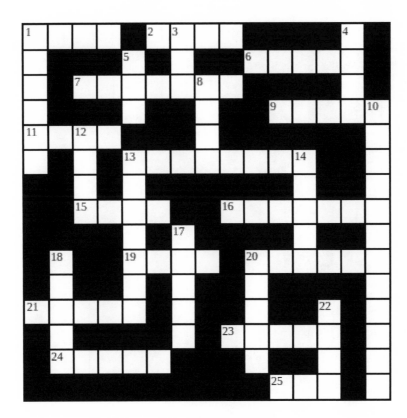

ACROSS

1. Vague; misty (4)
2. Wall in (4)
6. More timid (5)
7. The excellence of timbre (7)
9. Crete's capital before heraklion (5)
11. That's something ___! (4)
13. Like gen. tom thumb (8)
15. Well-used (4)
16. Shook (7)
19. Throw below deck, say (4)
20. Like many cheeses and tablets (6)
21. Gaelic goblin (5)
23. Goods depository (5)
24. Woodworker's pin (5)
25. They oversee the grand canyon: (abbr.) (3)

DOWN

1. Sweetened (var.) (6)
3. ___ possidetis (as you possess, at law) (3)
4. Charge without rupee? (4)
5. Political grp. (3)
8. Remove excess (4)
10. Self-taught (12)
12. Killed (archaic) (4)
13. Victorian beach where harold holt disappeared (7)
14. Wildlife expert jack (5)
17. Sequence of nude portraits in retrospective held by painter (5)
18. Araceous (5)
20. Panna or terra follower (5)
22. Prizms and storms (4)

Crossword Number 76

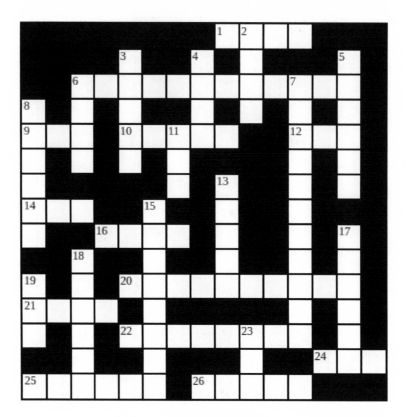

ACROSS

1. Miss williams and namesakes (4)
6. Sustained (12)
9. Parry sound nhl hero (3)
10. Beginning for graph (5)
12. Evidence of an expenditure: (abbr.) (3)
14. Post-season baseball (3)
16. Oates' singing partner (4)
20. Not very professional (10)
21. As well as being little short of luxurious (4)
22. Tuning (8)
24. True ___! (slangy agreement) (3)
25. Causing one to need rest (6)
26. This mr's history, h. g. wells (5)

DOWN

2. '? girl!' ('all right!') (4)
3. Arles apple (5)
4. Roman de brut poet robert (4)
5. Proxy (6)
6. Virginal (4)
7. Staying (11)
8. Grayi element (6)
11. Cato's 1200 (3)
13. Helper traps black bear (5)
15. Taking (8)
17. Grand - (atlantic island) (6)
18. Shutter slat (6)
19. Black - (3)
23. ___ follow the sun by the beatles (3)

Crossword Number 77

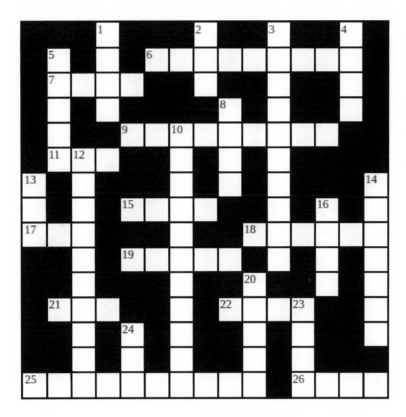

ACROSS

6. Crush five puerile characters with the last (9)
7. Fromage ingredient (4)
9. Enfeebling (9)
11. Hertz (3)
15. Alternative spelling for grassland in south africa (4)
17. Minuteclinic operator (3)
18. Plant of onion genus (6)
19. Teen king transposed it for the entire orchestra (5)
21. City in israel housing ben gurion international airport (3)
22. Done, and fast, extremely skilful (4)
25. Animal with a backbone (10)
26. Santa ? (some hot winds) (4)

DOWN

1. Result of driving on ice, perhaps (4)
2. Pier group?: (abbr.) (3)
3. Before (10)
4. Philatelist's concern, briefly (4)
5. Fool mechanic accepts old mexican (5)
8. Silents' theda - (4)
10. Advertisement paster (11)
12. Toy boy a mum loves to interrupt (10)
13. Cage digitally inserted into many a movie as a joke nowadays (3)
14. Hospital social worker (7)
16. Who's who paragraphs (4)
20. Trump's vice president (5)
23. Indian cooking implement (4)
24. Three, in torino (3)

Crossword Number 78

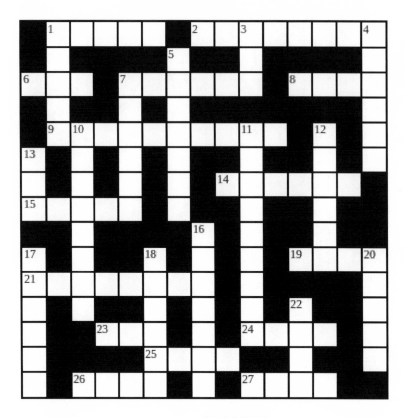

ACROSS

1. French town known for mustard (5)
2. Feeling awfully tense holding one set of holy works (8)
6. Utah beach craft (3)
7. Northern suburb of chicago (6)
8. South american parrot (4)
9. Humidity (10)
14. Taxi signaler (6)
15. Shrill, trilled sound (5)
19. Limb of a bird (4)
21. John ___, politician (8)
23. Pro baseball player from chicago (3)
24. Swallow nervously, after commercial setback (4)
25. Listen to mom, say (4)
26. Camera bag item (4)
27. Description of rustic life (4)

DOWN

1. Italian noblemen (5)
3. ? valley, san francisco (3)
4. Belonging to an incisor or molar, say (6)
5. Astute change of topic, being out to corner one! (7)
7. Flying bird, at times (6)
10. Overthrowing rout drew blood and agitated (8)
11. Marine's brutal, taking area with force (9)
12. Eyes: latin (6)
13. Alphabet's opening letters (3)
16. Spoke slowly and solemnly (7)
17. Cluster of genes (6)
18. Jazz groups (6)
20. Observer of stars, e.g. (5)
22. Criticize with scathing severity (4)

Crossword Number 79

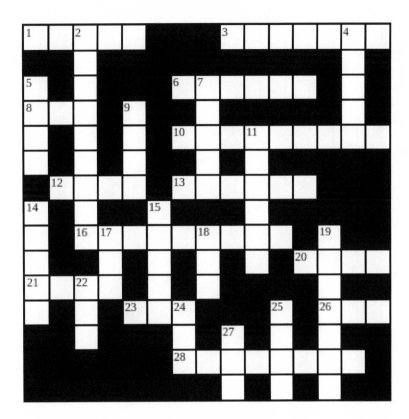

ACROSS

1. One of the ionian islands (5)
3. Moslem woman's veil (7)
6. Sandwich - it's old now (6)
8. Get rid of hatchet (3)
10. Application (9)
12. Toronto's famous 'casa' attraction (4)
13. Unpopular soviet leader visiting a german pow camp ... (6)
16. Doggedly persistent (9)
20. The first h in hanukkah (4)
21. Cops investigate cops on this (___ of duty) (4)
23. Old sitcom the doris ___ show (3)
26. Fairy tale giant's word (3)
28. Removal, erasure (8)

DOWN

2. Mississippi steamer, e.g. (9)
4. Poise, for a model (5)
5. God may absolve really stupid leaders (4)
7. Like jell-o that's not quite ready (5)
9. Melanesian basketwork palm (4)
11. Tabbouleh ingredient (6)
14. Anthony of 'boston public' (5)
15. Membrane of grasses (5)
17. Thieves disregard this errant female (3)
18. I copy extremes when cold (3)
19. Feudal labour (7)
22. Nonaccidental injury (3)
24. Letter of the hebrew alphabet (3)
25. Liberal ___ (4)
27. 2002 winter olympics venue, briefly (3)

Crossword Number 80

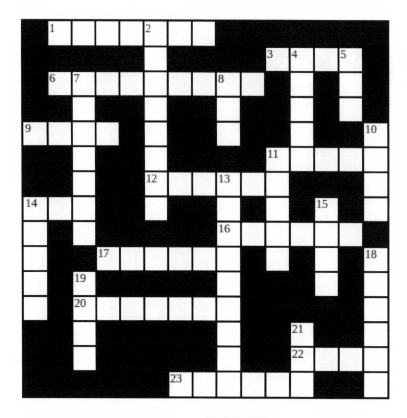

ACROSS

1. One displaying agony or anger snarled (7)
3. Pets turn out to be a blight (4)
6. Greek equivalent of the roman goddess venus (9)
9. House renovator of note (4)
11. Tawed leather (5)
12. Big bird dog (6)
14. Sheep-eating n.z. parrot (3)
16. ___ test (6)
17. Type of sweet (6)
20. Pass 51 from french crash (7)
22. Eye, in essen (4)
23. One spying on others for pleasure (6)

DOWN

2. To find tumour, doctor means to hold surgery close to hospital (8)
4. Best forty latin sounds (5)
5. Cruise around hollywood solution in next week's classifieds (3)
7. Philippine island separating sulu sea from south china sea (7)
8. Dress up as necessary to get to gateshead (3)
10. Ancient town in n africa (4)
11. It has its pluses and minuses, briefly (5)
13. Measuring out letter y takes one (9)
14. 1955 physics nobelist (5)
15. 12 words with king's 17 (4)
18. Eg, a lamb chop (6)
19. Adrenocorticotropic hormone (4)
21. A sailor (coll) (3)

Crossword Number 81

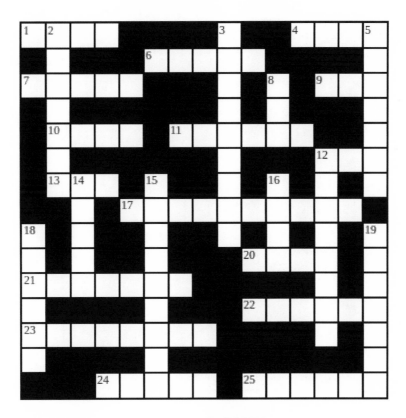

ACROSS

1. Girl invited into the garden in song (4)
4. Move suddenly (inf) (4)
6. Hood-shaped anatomical part (5)
7. Ending for snub (5)
9. Sum, shortly (3)
10. Attempt to cover front of neck with tie (4)
11. Cause distress to public school (6)
12. How to say yes in france (3)
13. Cancel that key (3)
17. Peel off (10)
20. Any thin strip of wood (4)
21. Cause amazement when rags get out of order (7)
22. Santa fe's last article (6)
23. Political efforts as victim is maltreated (8)
24. Part of a building for accommodating the old (5)
25. Nonconformist (6)

DOWN

2. Bio 101 studies (7)
3. Villainous (9)
5. Attack vermin mostly with big stick (7)
8. World war ii movie letters from ___ jima (3)
12. Best at yelling (8)
14. Woman's robe of ancient greece (5)
15. Mental quickness (9)
16. Male graduate upholding english novel (4)
18. Yoke (animals) (s. afr.) (6)
19. Brainwashed sorts, in slang (7)

Crossword Number 82

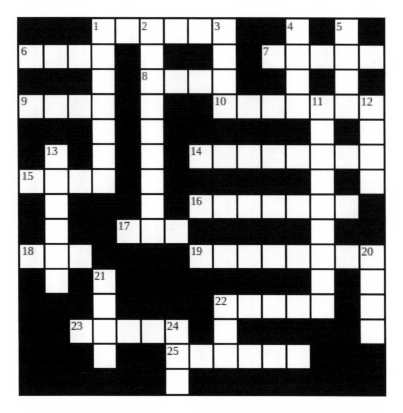

ACROSS

1. Laboured (6)
6. State donny and marie hail from (4)
7. Medicinal worm (5)
8. ___ te kanawa (4)
9. Snazzy coating (4)
10. Critic is after bob - run! (7)
14. Coaxing (8)
15. Inferior supporter backing fulham at first (4)
16. Like dali's art (7)
17. Eucharist wafers receptacle (3)
18. The phoenix (3)
19. Elderly state (8)
22. Like a toy piano's sound (5)
23. Belief in a 'watchmaker' god (5)
25. King after ethelred (6)

DOWN

1. Stop (something) working (7)
2. Ungracefully (9)
3. Sots' offenses, for short (4)
4. Reportedly beloved animals (4)
5. Spots cane construction (4)
11. Trip round museum and cathedral in secret? (9)
12. Gp. of battalions (4)
13. British certainly getting upper class cross in french town (6)
20. Honshu city (4)
21. It's northwest of provo (4)
22. Sir ___ jones, 22a's fellow judge on the voice uk, series three (3)
24. Ram measure (3)

Crossword Number 83

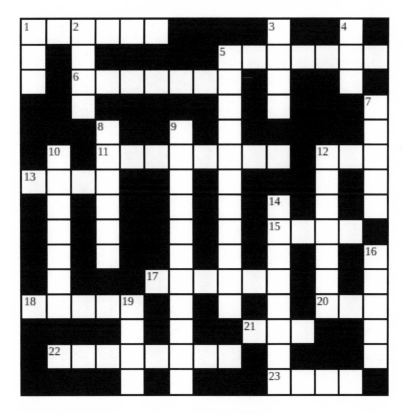

ACROSS

1. Rialto isn't in illustration and that's a snub (6)
5. Knowing route in part of london (7)
6. Thrown away (7)
11. Design new exercise in bowling (8)
12. Online id addresses (3)
13. Wax: french (4)
15. Traveled by train (4)
17. Stop row about greek character (6)
18. Scotland is not part of dysfunctional link-up (5)
20. Mean sea level: (abbr.) (3)
21. Prefix for mass or tech (3)
22. Occult doctrine (8)
23. Plant, avens (4)

DOWN

1. Desk well content (3)
2. Bad air procedure in front of surgeon general (4)
3. Freq. test giver (4)
4. James or hudson on a canada map (3)
5. Sorry (11)
7. Field trip vehicles (5)
8. American fuel order is handy (6)
9. University post (11)
10. Basin near a sink (7)
12. Corrosion resistant metal (7)
14. Tanning (8)
16. Money (for suckers?) (5)
19. Birth a lamb (4)

Crossword Number 84

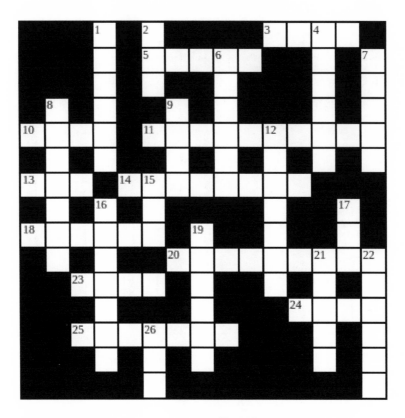

ACROSS

3. Griddlebaked indian bread (4)
5. Quiet for a gun they say (5)
10. Decorative container for flowers (4)
11. Simplify (10)
13. Common attached file (3)
14. Pertaining to a lower noble (8)
18. Warden (6)
20. Waterside (9)
23. Genus of maple tree (4)
24. Nitrogeneous waste from the body (4)
25. Dessert craftsman (7)

DOWN

1. Apartment provider (6)
2. Health ins. choice. (3)
4. Iranian city known for its carpets (6)
6. Newspaper feature (6)
7. Too-inquisitive person (5)
8. Ridge that may bump boat bottoms (7)
9. Unsmiling (4)
12. Mineral below orthoclase on the mohs scale (7)
15. Like many a dict. (3)
16. Resort near colchester (7)
17. Editor bradlee of the washington post (3)
19. Don't remember (6)
21. Annoyed pirate's utterance! (5)
22. Uninteresting (6)
26. Really good buddy, in texts (3)

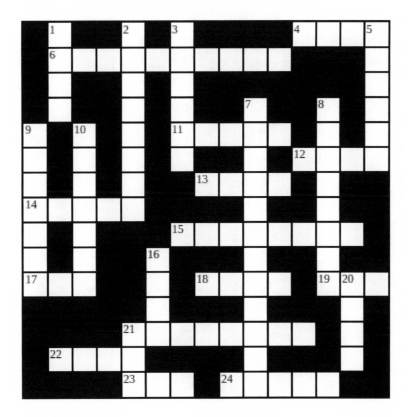

ACROSS

4. Short and detached, in music: (abbr.) (4)
6. Protests as job notices are wrong (10)
11. The bourne identity director doug (5)
12. Shed, like a reptile (4)
13. Hindu widow has material in short supply (4)
14. Wizard comics seen round university (5)
15. William ___, us nobel prize-winning novelist (8)
17. Musician clark (3)
18. Fork out to cover student drama (4)
19. Red club (3)
21. Breathing with difficulty, take a turn short on energy (8)
22. Word before pool or splicing (4)
23. Auction wager (3)
24. Leaf-eating moth (5)

DOWN

1. Be wolfish (4)
2. Penetrable (8)
3. Severe set involved with cathedral city (6)
5. Conservative doctor backing healthy sweet (6)
7. Singing (12)
8. Lack of (8)
9. More squalid (7)
10. Brave party that's revolting against gutless thuggery (7)
16. Hebrew letter (4)
20. Fools do gaffes regularly (4)
21. Information source, with the (3)

Crossword Number 86

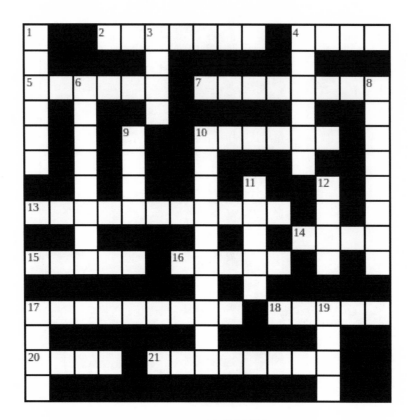

ACROSS

2. Division into two opposed aspects (7)
4. Dark side, metaphorically (4)
5. Oscar-winner rita (6)
7. Perforated pan (8)
10. Huntsman (6)
13. East london district (11)
14. Dependable as a clever ruse (4)
15. Five parts of a limerick (5)
16. Poi-producers (5)
17. Digestive medicine for cat in african country is fashionable (9)
18. New version of a song, perhaps (5)
20. Synthetic rubber (4)
21. Dubious (8)

DOWN

1. Tried out, as a product (6)
3. Stratford-upon-___ : shakespeare's place of birth (4)
4. Sweetened, in a way (6)
6. Put communist pointer to the east on the drawing board (8)
8. Yawed (8)
9. Vessel for roses, say (4)
10. Breakaway, seceding (10)
11. Notes taken down for future use (5)
12. Nea part: (abbr.) (4)
17. Port's opposite, on a boat: (abbr.) (4)
19. Evolutionary biologist ernst (4)

Crossword Number 87

ACROSS

2. Local bird gets fish beside river in abingdon (7)
4. Fought for one's honour, maybe (6)
7. Egyptian queen of all gods (3)
9. Emetic (6)
10. What many an old couch does (3)
11. Wind-blown pointer (4)
12. Dog many recalled (4)
13. Time units of sixty minutes (5)
15. Limb part (7)
20. Repeated (7)
21. Prevented the success of (6)
22. Stubborn seuss character (3)
23. Cricket side's knock covered by leader in guardian newspaper (9)

DOWN

1. (greek myth.) goddess of the earth (6)
3. Interrupt, offering copper money (5)
4. Sharp bend or angle (6)
5. He makes clear letter clearer (9)
6. Unfilled positions (9)
7. Very small in scale (4)
8. Colorful fishes (7)
13. Connecticut's capital (8)
14. Vote predictor (4)
16. Threat husband dismissed - pleasant surprise (5)
17. ... saved ___ penny earned (3)
18. Assembly of old women's one to beat! (5)
19. Room in a harem (4)

Crossword Number 88

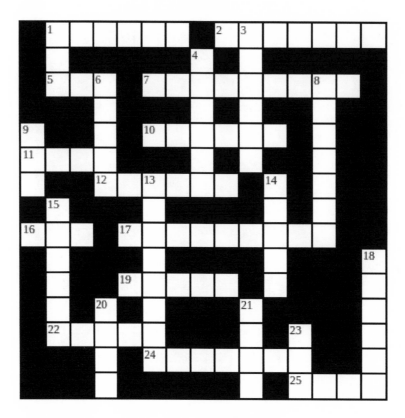

ACROSS

1. More likely to loaf (6)
2. It flies by, leaving celebrity confused (7)
5. Deviate erratically from a set course (3)
7. Former municipal borough now part of the london borough of brent (9)
10. ___ cupid, song released by connie francis in 1958 (6)
11. Class (4)
12. Potential fraternity pledge (6)
16. Angkor ___ (cambodian site) (3)
17. Voluptuous (9)
19. Name on the 2008 republican ticket (5)
22. Ender for auto or con (5)
24. Give the dye another try (7)
25. Maine city or river (4)

DOWN

1. Grassland meadow (3)
3. Louisiana parish (6)
4. Santa fe's last article (6)
6. Communion element (5)
8. Hermit or recluse (7)
9. Grand ___ (wine making phrase) (3)
13. Stamp bearing queen and queen rat (8)
14. Strongly push against wearing footwear (5)
15. Like the meter in sonnets (6)
18. Historic mormon settlement in illinois (6)
20. Lawd, could he produce movies! (anag.) (4)
21. Fused refuse that separates out from a metal during smelting (4)
23. Young ___ (small fry) (3)

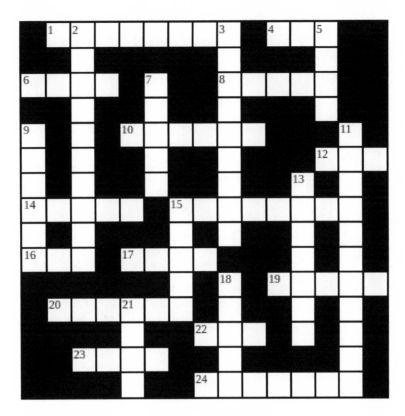

ACROSS

1. Name large ship the irishman (8)
4. Rhode island reds, e.g. (3)
6. Nba star anthony's nickname (4)
8. Some early photos in australia begin with this tint (5)
10. Revolutionary agreement court's thrown out (6)
12. Cricket term: (abbr.) (3)
14. Indian stringed instrument (5)
15. Barrel that is housing pet, a sea creature (8)
16. Post-season baseball (3)
17. Key related to f maj. (4)
19. Nerve agent (5)
20. Oom paul (6)
22. ___ zedong, chinese communist leader (3)
23. Sunnite moslem (4)
24. Be behind counter in bank, in great style (7)

DOWN

2. Vice versa (10)
3. Withholding (9)
5. Ending of many dutch place names (4)
7. Miss ___, lucie manette's governess in a tale of two cities (5)
9. Behave abjectly (6)
11. Generously (11)
13. Revenge for return on investment (7)
15. A person or thing that tries (5)
18. Dr. norman vincent ___ (5)
21. Dole cheque (4)

Crossword Number 90

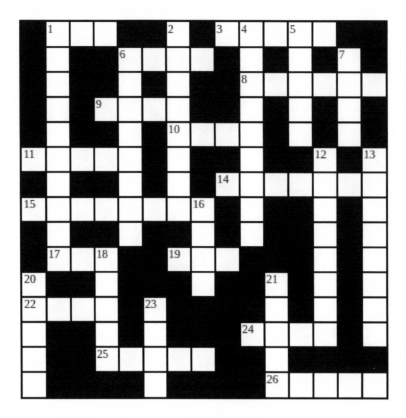

ACROSS

1. Pres.'s $ grp. (3)
3. Way to lay it on (5)
6. Some are sprayed on (4)
8. Lying university head featuring in column (6)
9. River in the ukraine (4)
10. Fly larva (4)
11. Cartoon art from japan (5)
14. Legislator, essentially (7)
15. Wrinkled (8)
17. Homeland channel (3)
19. Hawaiian tree (3)
22. Stone tomb (4)
24. Disappear, as symptoms (4)
25. Weaver film (5)
26. 1981 thriller, the postman always rings ___ (5)

DOWN

1. Progressions (10)
2. Impolite (8)
4. Rolling in cash, yet exhibiting doubt (9)
5. Clickety-___ (5)
6. Restrained and looking embarrassed after breaking teeth (8)
7. Throw, on the prairies (4)
12. Cheapest accommodation (8)
13. French brandy variety (8)
16. Promise returning mist in scotland (4)
18. Romae portus, urbs ad exitum tiberis sita, o clades! (5)
20. Kaddish setting (5)
21. Stumped, after judge's secret meeting (5)
23. Application specific integrated circuit (4)

Crossword Number 91

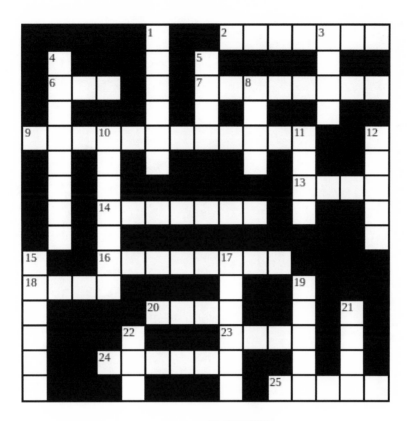

ACROSS

2. Becomes thiner (7)
6. Not being fit, it's what 'e must rise (3)
7. Working (8)
9. Not doubt (12)
13. Hawkeye's home (4)
14. Departed french city, abandoning an undiscovered state (7)
16. This powder? somehow manages to get one settled inside (8)
18. Fire truck necessity (4)
20. Ivory coast group (4)
23. Regret bringing in labour's first law (4)
24. Bring back, as a fashion (6)
25. Ameliorator (5)

DOWN

1. Post-sunset rainfall (6)
3. Rank-smelling (4)
4. The foam flower (8)
5. Compressed file format : (abbr.) (4)
8. Argentine rocker fito ___ (4)
10. Rock trio with the 1996 single what i got (7)
11. Little tantrum (4)
12. To drink heartily or in a draught (5)
15. A score and decade (6)
17. Hoarder's way to acquire gold sovereign (6)
19. Indian stringed instrument (5)
21. Harp's ancient kin (4)
22. Atop, for short (3)

Crossword Number 92

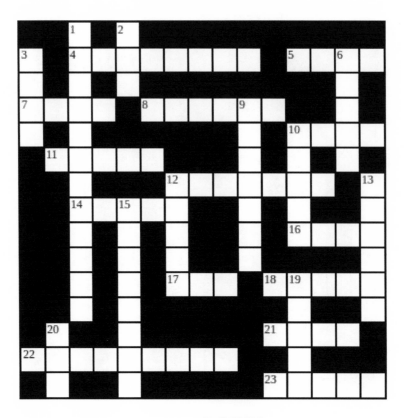

ACROSS

4. The good ___; 2016 james caan film (8)
5. Ape roger (4)
7. That's not for - say (4)
8. Two female sheep fret about their posterity (6)
10. Chief sobs uncontrollably (4)
11. Difficult to include old stock (5)
12. Scales on an animal or plant (7)
14. Motor collision (5)
16. Eel in traps repelled (4)
17. Tel. add-on (3)
18. Game to leave after a writer turns up (5)
21. Type of 11 repeated in the rocky horror picture show? (4)
22. I would back loud form of jazz spreading (9)
23. Pair of early communications satellites (5)

DOWN

1. Flattery (12)
2. Cover for a pot (3)
3. Shapeless chunk (4)
6. Temporary wait while father gets the habit (5)
9. Artist tours arab republic (7)
10. Tuba material (5)
12. Method that carries a stigma (5)
13. Develop again (6)
15. Spending less than budget, say (8)
19. One of three patriarchs from two different 5s (5)
20. Compete for metro canada (3)

Crossword Number 93

ACROSS

1. Onomatopoeia (7)
4. Youtube journal (4)
8. Like many an aarp mem. (3)
9. Preliminary heat (9)
10. Radio city's design style, informally (4)
12. Cut / hack (4)
13. Mode of walking (4)
14. Tire (8)
18. Style of chicken (8)
19. Place for a film king (4)
21. Flock of mallards (4)
23. Whirligigs (8)

DOWN

2. Command (archaic) (4)
3. Pacific island sorcery (4)
4. What a sentry keeps (5)
5. It may be applied to a tennis ball (8)
6. Alcohol arrest, briefly (3)
7. A shudder (4)
9. ___ street, imaginary place where debtors live (5)
11. Partner (10)
12. Meeting in one point (10)
15. Three ways modern (3)
16. Chief town in eastern nigeria (5)
17. ___ n bake (5)
20. Part of heater is known to be a hazard (4)
21. Madonna's first husband's initials-sharers (3)
22. Brand-name disinfectant (inits) (3)

Crossword Number 94

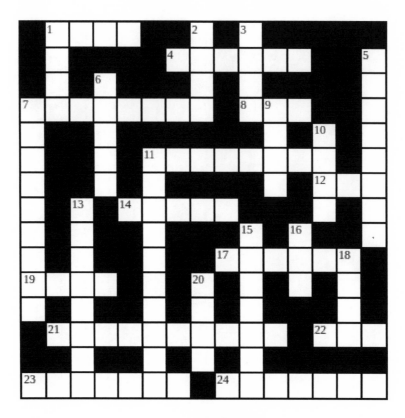

ACROSS

1. Fantastic!, for short (4)
4. Sheep gets in more trouble (6)
7. Plotted a conspiracy (8)
8. With freshness (3)
11. Mixed martial arts in upscale abode, without underwear (8)
12. Extremely high fre quency: (abbr.) (3)
14. Lacking leadership (5)
17. A scholar was in session about the front of the army (6)
19. Gees preceders (4)
21. Ridicule (10)
22. Big style, briefly (3)
23. Lower (7)
24. Try trampoline initially during various team exercises (7)

DOWN

1. Drug doctors supply (4)
2. Licentious welsh leader's taken out (4)
3. Be impolite about east anglian town (4)
5. Too much to drink (8)
6. An estate landowner in scotland (5)
7. More stingy (9)
9. Oscar winner for milk (4)
10. (missing clue) (4)
11. United (10)
13. Puffed out (hair) (8)
15. Retailer founded by terence conran (7)
16. ? -relief (3)
18. Russian emperor (var. spelling) (4)
20. Former new york city mayor ed who wrote murder mysteries (4)

Crossword Number 95

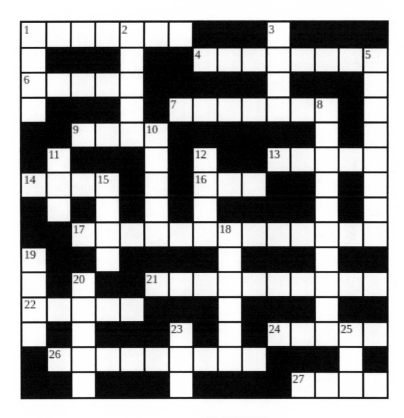

ACROSS

1. Of the '50s or '60s (7)
4. Wrapping (8)
6. Chief town in eastern nigeria (5)
7. Poisonous (7)
9. 'close call!' (4)
13. A fairly short period (5)
14. It can turn pumpkin into carriage (4)
16. Charles on the piano (3)
17. Mediation (13)
21. Cotton sari crumpled in drawer (10)
22. Hauling into court (5)
24. Carries out (archaic) (5)
26. Citrus drink like lemonade (9)
27. King, one to act crazy! (4)

DOWN

1. Bite preventer (4)
2. Mideast unitarians (5)
3. Cat's sound of pleasure (4)
5. From funafuti (8)
8. Question (10)
10. It's used to prevent movement on the western border (5)
11. Ger. state (3)
12. Fall in drops; dribble (4)
15. Denial (fr.) (4)
18. Very big to incline to port (6)
19. Nearly all medical officer's time (4)
20. Reading unit (5)
23. Book end (3)
25. Nashville sch (3)

Crossword Number 96

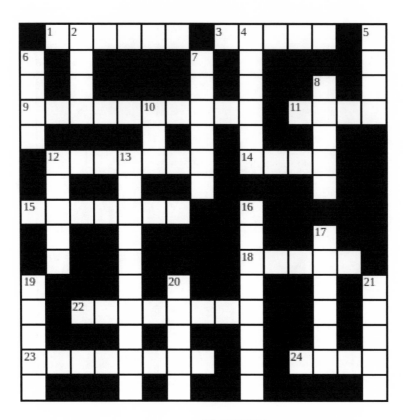

ACROSS

1. Lochte rival (6)
3. Venezuelan river (5)
9. Prudent (10)
11. Elizabethan madam (4)
12. Sort of ace duet used to impart learning (7)
14. Military assistant : (abbr.) (4)
15. Wool grease (7)
18. You ___ judge (5)
22. Tranquil or serene (8)
23. Stooping in reverence (8)
24. Galvanizing metal (4)

DOWN

2. Man of hannover (4)
4. National flower of south africa (6)
5. With pleasure, clasp pen (4)
6. Another name for a latvian (4)
7. (missile) target searcher (6)
8. Boy in the courtyard (5)
10. Southern reservoir mgr. (3)
12. Israeli seaport (5)
13. As relating to the arts and intellectual achievements (10)
16. Walking lamely (8)
17. Equal-sided parallelograms (6)
19. Small baleen whale (5)
20. Cold-weather forecast word (5)
21. Rolls-___ (jet engine maker) (5)

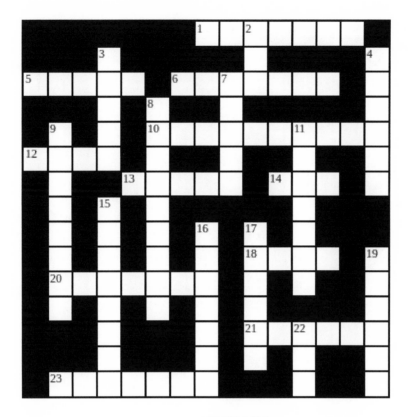

ACROSS

1. Party within a party (7)
5. Kitchen floor coverings (5)
6. Serving as a pilot (7)
10. Illustrate (10)
12. Used by the sick, abused for the kick (4)
13. Mischievous pranks (var.) (5)
14. Napoleon's title: (abbr.) (3)
18. Ambulance-calling situation: (abbr.) (4)
20. ___ roosevelt, first lady of the united states from 1933-1945 (7)
21. One hundred plunges in river seems extreme. it's too much! (6)
23. Visual (7)

DOWN

2. Fish caught do wriggle (3)
3. Not old! (5)
4. () marks, for short (6)
7. Intestinal obstruction (5)
8. Yielding (9)
9. Separated (8)
11. Cleared away / killed (7)
15. Seek a man (anag.) - one with an intimate connection? (8)
16. Rub (7)
17. Younger beef animal (6)
19. Treachery decapitation takes place - that's logical (6)
22. Brain liquid [acronym] (3)

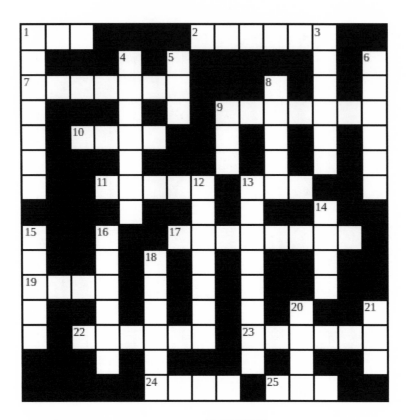

ACROSS

1. Mlb stat trio (3)
2. Western crew makes impact (6)
7. Obtain, get hold of (7)
9. Small glacier-formed hill (7)
10. 1992 film, a river ___ through it (4)
11. *have membership in (5)
13. President's financial grp. (3)
17. More springy (8)
19. ___ a (no) (4)
22. Tallying (6)
23. Square root of dieciseis (6)
24. Finally sigh with measure of warmth over miserable person (4)
25. Govt. loan backer (3)

DOWN

1. Lie mars practicality (7)
3. Videos (6)
4. Foolish people (7)
5. Part of rom: (abbr.) (3)
6. More than one over one over the eight (6)
8. Not all sliced up - left in two (5)
9. Letters for whittyorhess (3)
12. Catching it's not positive around carol (7)
13. Reduce length of one spade for example (8)
14. Ancient briton (var) (4)
15. Region in southeastern europe (5)
16. Ohio city (6)
18. Inside layer (6)
20. 100,000 rupees (ind) (4)
21. If i were a ___ (beyonce song) (3)

Crossword Number 99

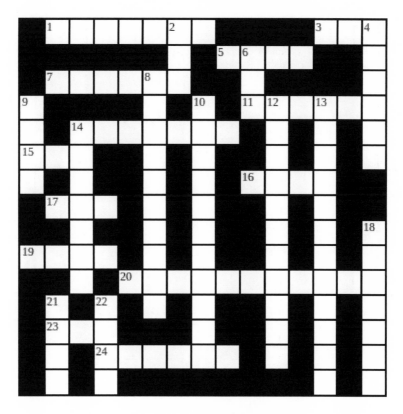

ACROSS

1. Large, solid (7)
3. Rail transit inits. (3)
5. Some backing free vote for change of course (4)
7. Pop music bribery (6)
11. Ecosystem components (6)
14. Twisting (7)
15. She's gotta have it creator/director spike (3)
16. Hist. assignment (4)
17. Keep movin'! (3)
19. Cavaliers player korver (4)
20. Ideal spacecraft-propulsion method (11)
23. Every bit of (3)
24. Books university set aside for records (6)

DOWN

2. By a route that passes through bolivia, finally (3)
4. City in southern turkey and the birthplace of saint paul (6)
6. Extremely high frequency: (abbr.) (3)
8. Suing (10)
9. Like a just-purchased house (4)
10. Tallstalked (11)
12. Uppish (11)
13. Cancelling out (12)
14. Comic opera in two acts by rossini, first performed in 1816 (7)
18. Word having stress on the last syllable (7)
21. The states bad bank. (4)
22. Paving-stone (4)

Crossword Number 100

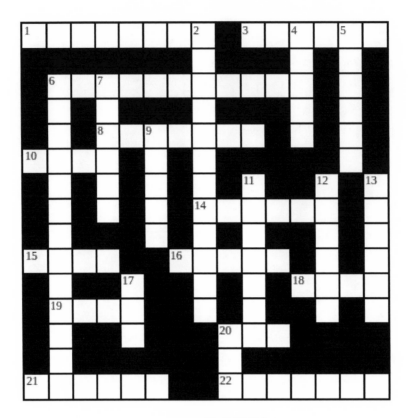

ACROSS

1. Makes obscure picture about eating prunes (8)
3. Fruit crop destroyer (6)
6. Unwoven (11)
8. Outfitting (7)
10. Twofer sales acronym (4)
14. What ___, or of any kind (6)
15. Informal hand grenade (4)
16. Ruhr city (5)
18. Girl invited into the garden in song (4)
19. ___ karenina (4)
20. Li'l edmonton transport (3)
21. Bee's quest (6)
22. Jump (7)

DOWN

2. Lie (12)
4. Iffy (5)
5. To undo or unfasten (6)
6. Obnoxious (13)
7. Rearrange equipment robber rejected (6)
9. Artist's painting surface (5)
11. Style (7)
12. Wintry (6)
13. Artificial; bogus (6)
17. Pouch one almost gets on being dismissed (3)
20. Captain's daily report (3)

Solutions

Solutions

Crossword Number 1

Crossword Number 2

Crossword Number 3

Crossword Number 4

Solutions

Crossword Number 5

Crossword Number 6

Crossword Number 7

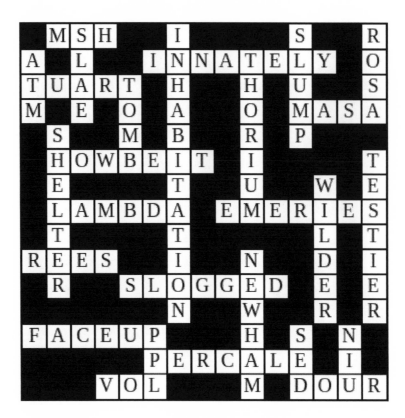

Crossword Number 8

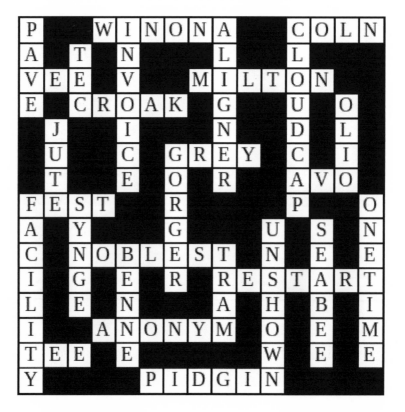

Crossword Number 9

Crossword Number 10

Crossword Number 11

Crossword Number 12

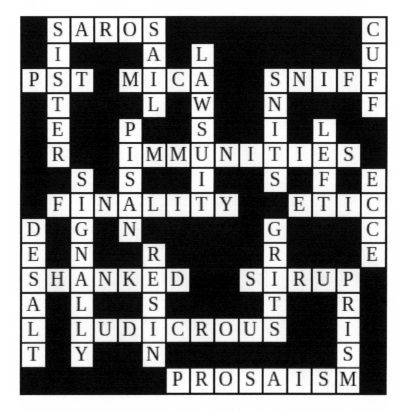

Crossword Number 13

Crossword Number 14

Crossword Number 15

Crossword Number 16

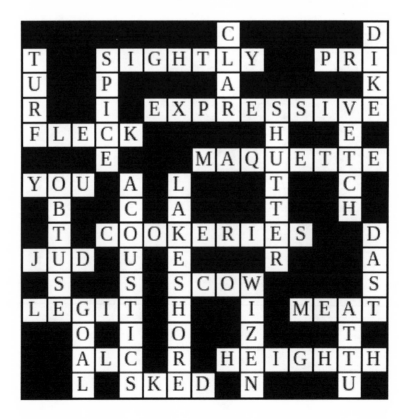

Crossword Number 17

```
  M         H   B     T U L E
S O B     W I E N I E
  J       W       R       F       N
  A       E P H E D R A       A   A
  V   S   E       D       I N S T
C E N T   R       P           A   I
O     O   S       E       F   S   C
A     C O E T A N E O U S         K
S     K   V       C       O   T   K
T     G A P E D           L   I
  U   D   R       D           C       T
  N   I   R       R A N S     D       A
  C   N   N       I       T   D       S
F A N G       G E N T L E F O L K
  S               A       N       W
```

Crossword Number 18

```
          C     P I P P I N
A U R O R A     T     U         W
G       O     P A R R I S H
R O T O             L     V     I
E U     P R O F I L E       N T H
E B     R         A     Y       E
D E     O         L             N
  R     V   R E M E D I E S     E
  L O P A         S             D
L S     L         C U             T
O I     P I X E L A T E D         O
A T     N         E   I           W
F       G     W A N L Y           E
E               V       O         R
R A N K     N E E D F U L L Y
```

Crossword Number 19

Crossword Number 20

Crossword Number 21

Crossword Number 22

Crossword Number 23

Crossword Number 24

Crossword Number 25

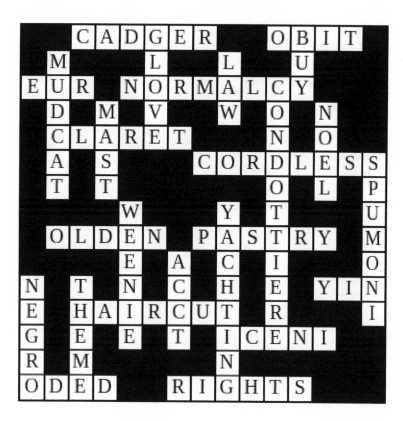

Crossword Number 26

Crossword Number 27

Crossword Number 28

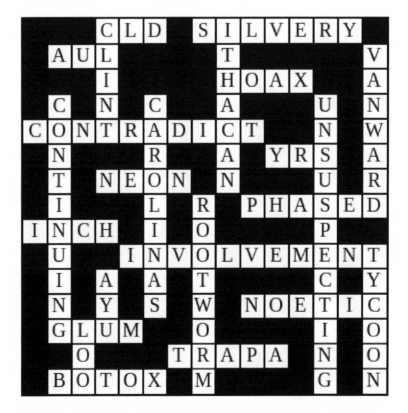

Solutions

Crossword Number 29

Crossword Number 30

Crossword Number 31

Crossword Number 32

Crossword Number 33

Crossword Number 34

Crossword Number 35

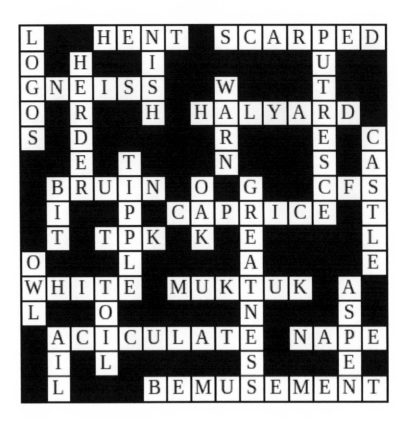

Crossword Number 36

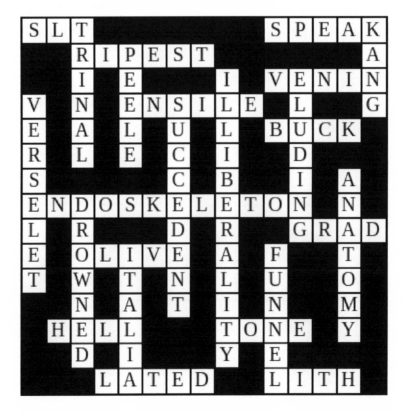

Crossword Number 37

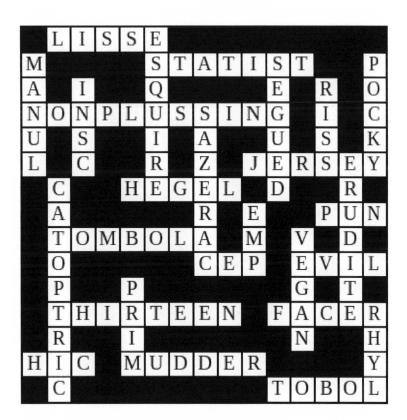

Crossword Number 38

Crossword Number 39

Crossword Number 40

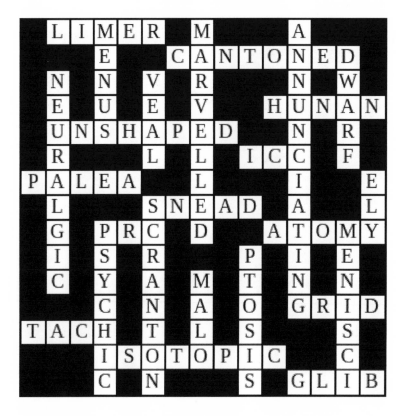

Crossword Number 41

```
  A G R I N           P
  A       E     L A M P R E Y S
  P U R L I E U     D
  P   U         M E O W   A N N
  O   G         I       T
  R   B     N O N B E L I E F
  T   Y         E           O
  I       P     S   U N S T O P
E O M     A     C   N       S
  N   P U N G E N T L Y   R
    H   S     G       A   A
I P A S     E   B     S   T
    R   T A X I   T E S T I S
D E E       T   E       O
    M A Q U I S   D E T E N T
```

Crossword Number 42

```
        C O M M O V E D
P     T           A   O
U R L   C O R R I V A L   U
N       G       I       D   V
G       G     Y   N   D   I
E     M A L L A R D   A D V T
N   A     E     N   I   R   A
C O M E T     N     C   M   E
E   E         A     A   S E X
  K N O B     S     T       R
    D   I N H A B I T A N C E
H     R     L   N   D   E
U N D E R   L   G   T   B
I         A D           U
  D E G R A D E R       F
                        F
```

Crossword Number 43

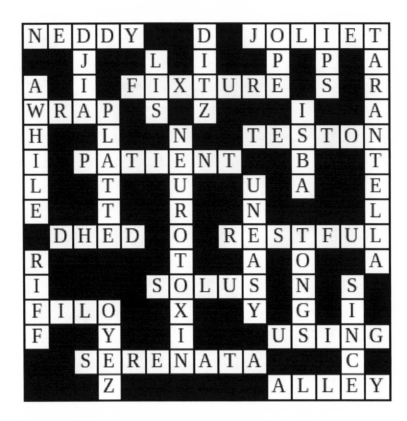

Crossword Number 44

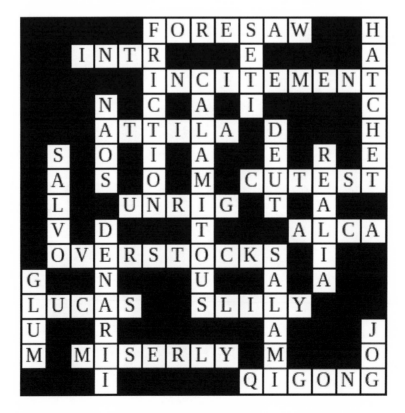

Crossword Number 45

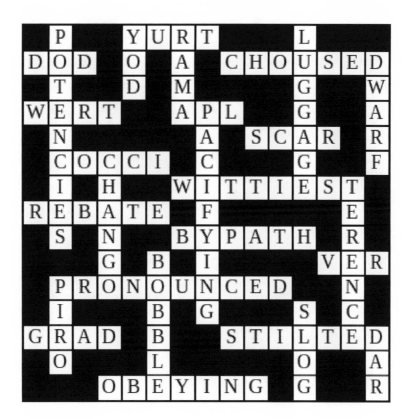

Crossword Number 46

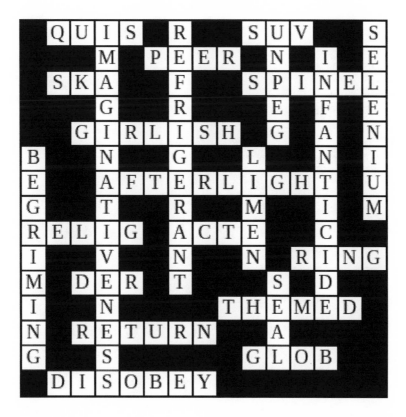

Crossword Number 47

Crossword Number 48

Crossword Number 49

Crossword Number 50

Crossword Number 51

Crossword Number 52

Crossword Number 53

```
N   C     F           C       B
I   A X I L       N   O       A
I   T     E R R A N D     C R U
P     M O W       P   E       T
I     M           P           E
C R O O K     S L E A Z I E R
K   N     I             X     P
    E     T       O   L I P I D
F R Y         G Y M       L   A
I   M A S S       N   T I D
D   A         S W I N G   C
O   K     O       V   D I C K
S   I   R E P R O     T
    N   F         R   L N D
F O G I E S   Y E A S T Y
```

Crossword Number 54

```
Y U C K Y     T S K       N
    L         N A G G E R E R
  L A N I E R O           V   G
    T             O       I   A
O U T     S O L I D   A N G L
    E     U       N   D   S   O
D U R A   P       G   I       O
  R       P   W       L   B   T
  A       U   I     W I R R A
K N O W E R   E           E
          A M N E S T I E D
  C R U E T           Z
  M       I       M   E
A D J   C O N V O L V E D
  R       N       M
```

Crossword Number 55

Crossword Number 56

Crossword Number 57

Crossword Number 58

Crossword Number 59

Crossword Number 60

Crossword Number 61

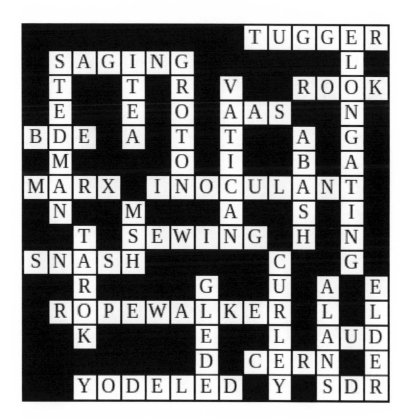

Crossword Number 62

Crossword Number 63

Crossword Number 64

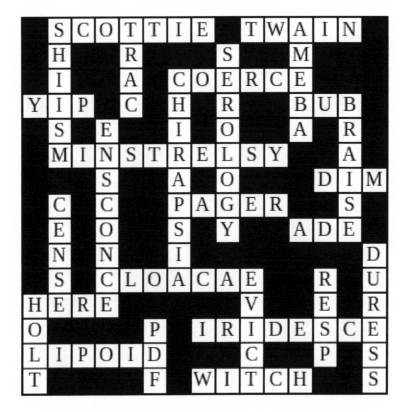

Crossword Number 65

Crossword Number 66

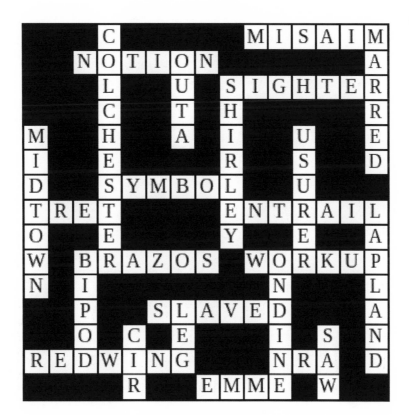

Crossword Number 67

Crossword Number 68

Crossword Number 69

Crossword Number 70

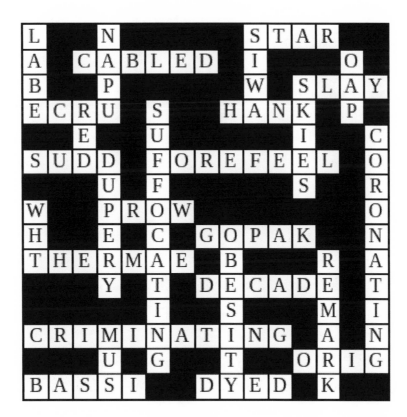

Crossword Number 71

Crossword Number 72

Crossword Number 73

Crossword Number 74

Crossword Number 75

Crossword Number 76

Crossword Number 77

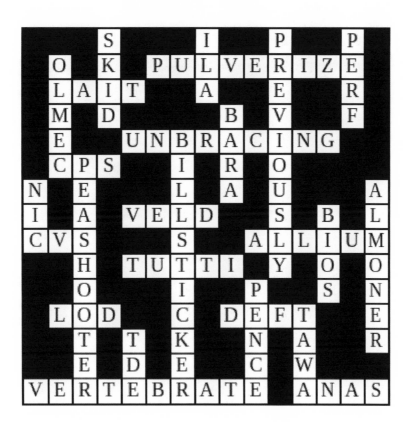

Crossword Number 78

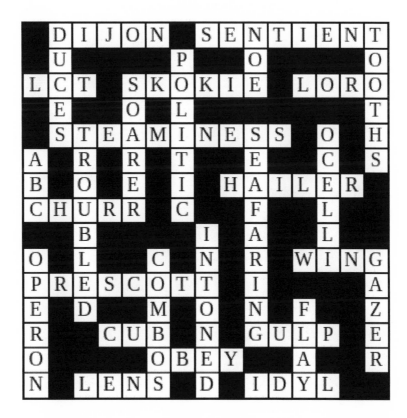

Crossword Number 79

Crossword Number 80

Crossword Number 81

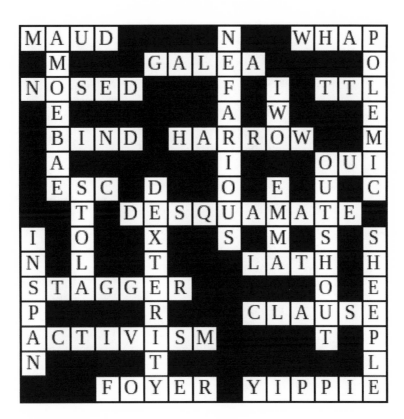

Crossword Number 82

Crossword Number 83

Crossword Number 84

Crossword Number 85

Crossword Number 86

Crossword Number 87

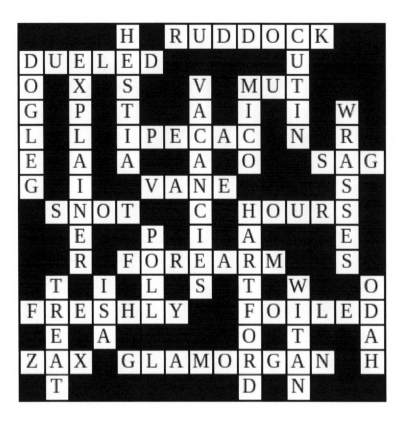

Crossword Number 88

Solutions

Crossword Number 89

Crossword Number 90

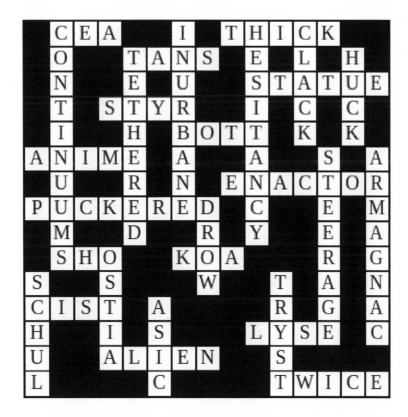

Crossword Number 91

Crossword Number 92

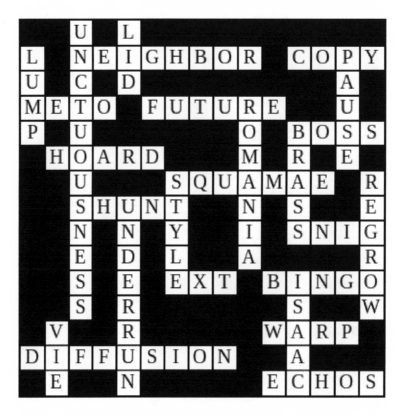

Crossword Number 93

Crossword Number 94

Crossword Number 95

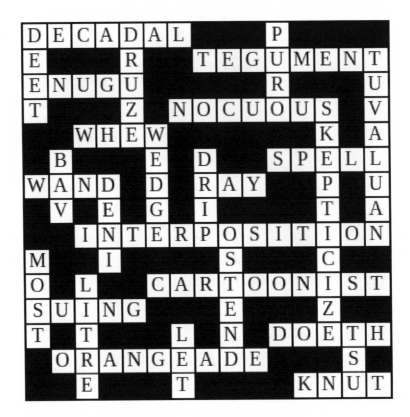

Crossword Number 96

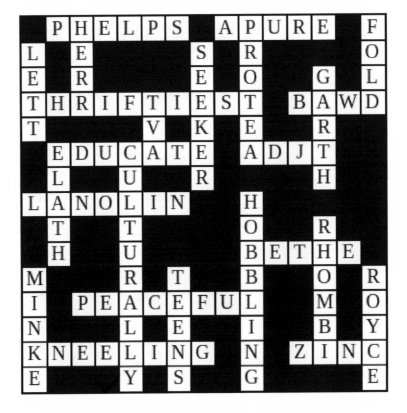

Solutions

Crossword Number 97

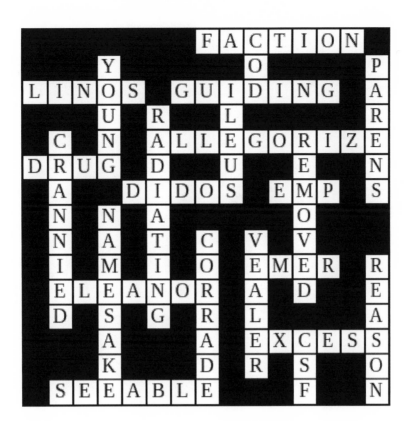

Crossword Number 98

Crossword Number 99

Crossword Number 100

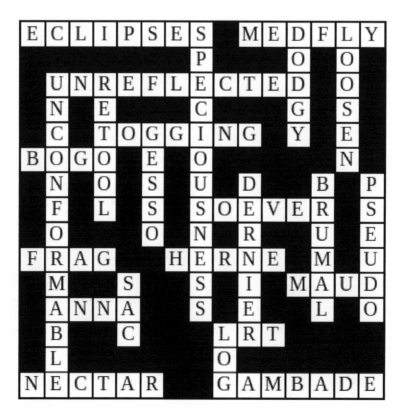